# The World of
# INSECTS

## BY ADRIANO ZANETTI

TRANSLATED FROM THE ITALIAN BY Catherine Atthill

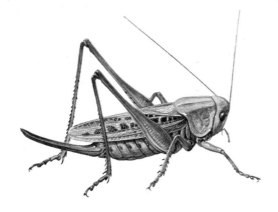

GALLERY BOOKS
An Imprint of W. H. Smith Publishers Inc.
112 Madison Avenue
New York City 10016

*Designers/Artists*
Illustrations drawn by Giambattista Bertelli together with Luciano Corbella:
10, 12a, 221; Piero Cozzaglio: 17a, 94a, da 234 a 251; Raffaele Curiel: 50; H.
Kacher: 165, 166-167, 169; Raffaello Segattini: 114a.

*Photographs*
Alberto Ancillotto: 71, 123, 128, 160, 161, 196-197b; Archives Rencontre:
38-39b; Mondadori: 16, 17b, 30, 35, 43, 114b, 115, 211, 228a, 229d; Carlo
Bevilacqua/Luisa Ricciarini: 39a, 51, 97a; I. Bucciarelli/Luisa Ricciarini:
138a, 194; Chaumeton, Jacana: 31a; Franco Frezzato: 31B, 37a, 153,
154a/b; Donato Giussani/Luisa Ricciarini: 14, 42-43c, 76, 77as; K.
Kohout/Tom Stack & Associates: 101b; O. Langini/Luisa Ricciarini: 216-
217; S. Lombardi/Luisa Ricciarini: 33b, 66, 77ad; Aldo Margiocco: 34, 58
(bottom right), 72, 81a, 97b, 180s, 214d, 215s, 217b; Giuseppe Mazza: 11,
12b, 15, 44, 61, 142, 149, 154c, 159, 164, 176, 177, 186b, 193, 214s; J.
Palmer: 105; Pictor: 13, 141b, 145, 186a, 203, 204; Folco Quilici: 215s;
Enrico Robba/Luisa Ricciarini: 34-35c, 58 (bottom right), 84-85, 117, 228b;
G. Tomsich/Luisa Ricciarini: 180-181, 226; Torquati: 199; Gianni Tortoli: 67,
111, 112-113; M.W.F. Tweedie/Bruce Coleman: 143.

**Library of Congress Cataloging in Publication Data**

Zanetti, Adriano.
    THE WORLD OF INSECTS.

    Translation of Il mondo degli insetti.
    Bibliography:   p. 252–3
    1.   Insects.   I.   Title.
QL467.Z3613     1979     595.7          79-1424

ISBN: 0-8317-9554-9

Printed and bound in Italy by Officine Grafiche of Arnoldo
Mondadori Editore, Verona.

This edition published by Gallery Books, a division of W.H. Smith Inc.,
112 Madison Avenue, New York, New York 10016.
Originally published by Abbeville Press, Inc.

# Contents

# Introduction

Most people have only the vaguest idea of what *'an insect'* really is and there can be few branches of natural history which are so sketchily understood. The very word *'insect'* usually suggests something harmful, dangerous, or at very least annoying. It makes you think of the mosquito's drone on a summer night, followed by the itch of its bite, or the loathsome cockroach scurrying along a wall. Or you remember some farmer cursing the insect which has arrived from America and ruined his potato crop. The Butterfly is an insect too, but it is too beautiful and likeable to be counted as such by the layman.

The insect world, this world of six-legged animals, is too small

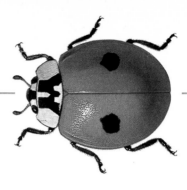

and complex to catch our attention, preoccupied as we are by so many large-scale concerns. Yet we need only look around carefully to find insects everywhere – under mounds of seaweed at the seaside, or on the snowline. No other group of animals are as adaptable as insects, and this means that they can survive where other animals perish, and eat what others reject. Where conditions are favourable, they are able to multiply in an alarming fashion. In a world in which man's encroachment threatens the survival of thousands of animal species, often only insects can stand up to them. It may well be that man's hatred of insects is explained by this great strength concealed by an appearance of fragility which makes man see insects as the only enemy in the animal kingdom which he cannot destroy, because the cost in terms of both effort and money is too great.

However, it is this tremendous capacity for adaptation to difficult environments which makes the insect world, far more than any other zoological group, an inexhaustible source of information for the specialist or layman. The study of entomology, the science of insects, has yielded an impressive body of facts, and continues to do so. It has made it possible to identify hundreds of thousands of different species, each with specialized mechanisms for the struggle for existence; it has shown subtle defensive and attacking devices, from the complex mimicry of butterflies to the chemical weapons of some Coleoptera; it reveals the fundamental differences between the insect and the human worlds. These differences occur on two different levels – the structure of insects and their life history. Words like heads, legs and eyes as applied to insects refer to structures which perform the same functions as the analagous organs in vertebrates, but in totally different way. Take, for example, the skeleton, the framework which supports the animal. In vertebrates it is internal and has the dual function of supporting the body and giving attachment to the muscles. In insects, on the other hand, it is external and also has a protective function. Some features of insects have substantial advantages over the equivalent apparatus in vertebrates. This is true of the respiratory system of tracheae which carries oxygen directly to the tissues, so that the animal does not need respiratory pigment. As for the life history of insects, the outstanding feature is the often total dissimilarity between the life of the insect as larva in the early stage, and as adult; habits and functions are quite different. With insects which undergo total metamorphosis, when the animal which hatches from the egg is quite different from the adult, the larva has a single purpose – eating; while the adult often simply has the function of reproduction. The change between the two stages involves a drastic transformation.

These animals, so different from us and from our 'relations' on the evolutionary family tree, are masters in many environments. They are constantly in competition with all vertebrates and it is worth noting that this struggle brings into opposition two different types of mechanism for reacting to stimuli; the essentially instinctive mechanisms of insects, and the vertebrate mechanism which, at different levels, can learn from and exploit experience. The most common relationship between vertebrates and insects is that of predator and prey. Many species of birds and even mammals are known to feed exclusively or mainly on insects. This forces insects to develop highly effective defence mechanisms, from rapid flight to the subtlest forms of mimicry. Often, however, the principal enemy of an insect species is another insect which, as predator or parasite, instinctively and unhesitatingly selects its victim. The relationships between species are complex and many-sided. A summer field which to us seems calm and peaceful is a scene of constant battle; the apparent calm is merely the result of an equilibrium. The insatiable appetite of leaf-eating insects, which could swiftly reduce the green expanse to a sterile environment, is counterbalanced by the action of innumerable small predators and parasites, the former ready to devour their prey, the latter to probe the bodies of other insect species and lay their eggs inside them. This complex system of relationships is the most outstanding feature of insect ecology, and the experts frequently have to confess that they are unable to discover the mechanisms by which it operates. The sheer size of the field to be explored and the alarming number of unsolved natural mysteries can at times be discouraging for the entomologist.

If the behaviour of plant-eating insects and their parasites seems obscure, the actions of scavengers are even more so. An enormous amount of organic material in our environment is not used directly by herbivorous animals – to understand this you have only to think of the leaves which collect in the woods in autumn. If this material was not used, much of the energy imprisoned in the living material by plants would not be released. The joint action of plants without chlorophyll and the lower animals – among them countless insects – makes it possible for this energy to be returned to the cycle. Creatures living in the leaf deposits of a wood have a continuous supply of material at their disposal and so do not particularly need to be able to move from place to place. However, insects which feed on dung and carrion need great mobility and skill in locating their food in order to survive. The ability of insects to move by flight and their highly refined sense organs make them particularly adapted for this job as nature's dustmen.

This outline of man's attitude to insects shows how distorted and subjective his view is, when it is logical to judge animals in their own terms. An animal is neither good nor bad, since it cannot be measured by human standards. And the fiercest carnivore would surely judge man more harshly than man judges him. Indeed, nature as a whole, the realm in which the forces of energy are balanced, has every reason to complain that man is an unnatural son.

9

### Groups related to Insects

Before dealing with insects themselves it is worth taking a look at the animals closest to them in structure and organization.

Insects belong to the vast group of Arthropoda, the most complex and specialized group of invertebrates. Although extremely varied in form, size and habits, arthropods have some important characteristics in common. The body consists of segments which are sometimes similar to one another but are usually very differentiated, so that the animal is divided into distinct parts (in the case of insects: head, thorax and abdomen).

Each segment may have a pair of limbs, which are generally used for locomotion, but may have further functions such as carrying food to the mouth. Finally, the arthropod body has an external skeleton rich in natural salts and certain organic substances which make it particularly tough. The Arthropoda are Earth's largest group of animals. They live in all environments.

In their attempts to identify the ancestors of the Arthropoda, the group of primitive animals from which they descend, zoologists generally turn to the Annelida, the group of segmental worms which includes the familiar earthworm and leech. However, the annelids closest to the arthropods are thought to be the polychaetae: these marine worms, which are able to stay on the seabed or be free-moving, have expansions

▼ Onychophora                                        Errant Polychaete ▶

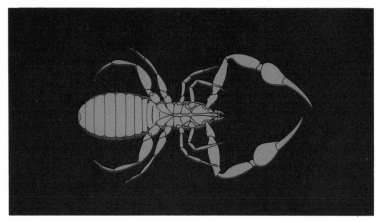

▲ Pseudoscorpion                                    ▼ Scorpion

known as parapodia, which to some extent resemble arthropods limbs. These marine worms are often brightly coloured.

The Onychophora are a group with characteristics which make them intermediate between Annelida and Arthropoda. They are worm-like creatures, found only in the Southern hemisphere, which live in damp places; however their fossilized ancestors, which had segmented bodies, were marine animals.

Among the oldest arthropod fossil remains are those of the Arachnida, suggesting that they have lived longest on Earth. The class includes animals as different as spiders, scorpions and mites, which all have four pairs of legs as a common characteristic. As well as these familiar animals the Arachnida include false scorpions, small arthropods which resemble scorpions in every respect except that they do not have the 'tail' and poison apparatus.

▼ Bird-eating Spider

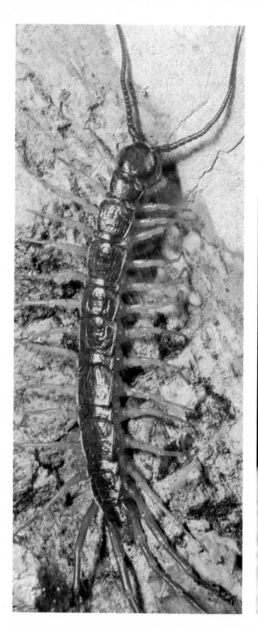

◀ Centipede

▼ Fiddler Crab

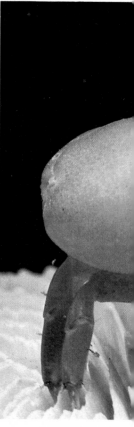

The name Myriapoda is used to cover all arthropods which do not have separate thorax and abdomen, but which have many pairs of legs. They are now subdivided into the Chilopoda or centipedes (for example, the genus *Lithobius*) which have one pair of legs for each body segment, and the Diplopoda or millipedes, two pairs of legs to each segment.

The Crustacea form a vast group of animals, the great majority of them aquatic. In addition to the few universally known species, such as crabs, lobsters and crayfish, crustaceans include an enormous number of small organisms found in marine and fresh water plankton.

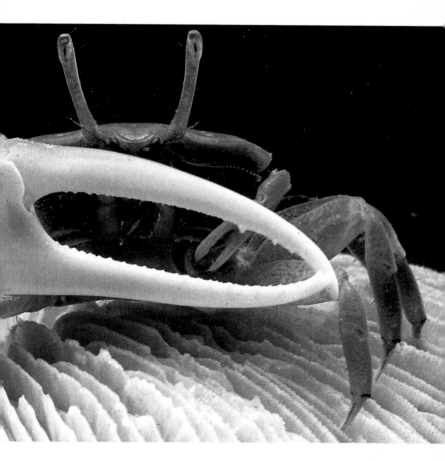

### Insect Fossils

Zoologists often make use of fossilized organisms in reconstructing the stages of animal evolution. A fossil is the modified remains of a plant or animal which has been preserved in sedimentary rock. The delicate structure of so many insects, due to the lack of mineral salts, has made fossilization difficult, but there is nevertheless a rich body of fossil evidence which indicates that there have been insects on Earth for at least 350 million years.

In the Palaeozoic period most insects belonged to the so-called primitive groups. The giant *Meganeura* deserve special mention: these were enormous dragonfly-like insects, with a

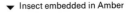
▼ Fossil Insect      ▼ Insect embedded in Amber

wing span of some 2 feet 6 inches (70 cm), which one can picture flying through the forests of tree-fern, the remains of which were to form coal deposits. More evolved insects, undergoing total metamorphosis, began to develop widely in the Mesozoic period, side by side with the flowering plants, with which many of them are associated.

However, the best finds are the many insects preserved in amber, trapped by this resin as it oozed out of conifers.

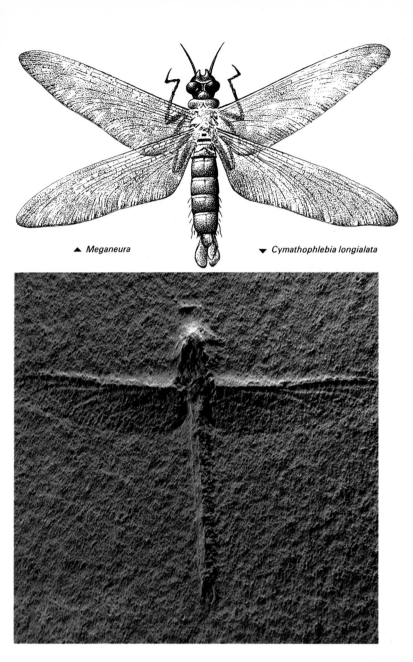

▲ Meganeura          ▼ Cymathophlebia longialata

17

# Structure

A segmented body is, as we have said, one of the main characteristics all arthropods have in common. In discussing insect structure we must first see what segmentation means in terms of insects and what modifications have occurred in the course of evolution. Insects have heterogeneous metamerism, that is to say they are subdivided into segments which are differentiated, one from another.

These parts of the body are different in function as well as in structure. The head is concerned with the capture of food and important sensory activities, the thorax with locomotion (and so has legs and wings), while the abdomen is equipped with the

reproductive apparatus. This division of labour gives an idea of how 'decentralized' insects' bodies are – a characteristic which will be even more obvious when we examine the nervous system.

The insect head consists of seven segments which are, however, so completely fused that the head seems to be a single part. It has appendages, some forming the mouth parts, others serving sensory functions. The mouth parts consist of the labrum (upper lip), the mandibles (the jaws), and the labium (lower lip). The sensory function is performed by the antennae, compound eyes and simple ocelli, while there are also many hairs concerned with the sense of touch.

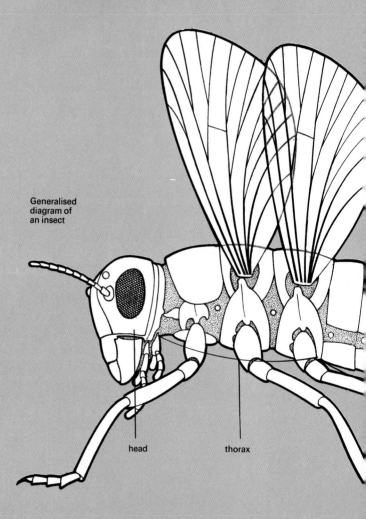

Generalised
diagram of
an insect

head　　　　　　　　　thorax

The thorax always consists of three segments, known as the prothorax, mesothorax and metathorax; each carries a pair of legs and the last two may also have wings. The most primitive insects are apterous or wingless. Many insects belonging to orders considered to be more evolved are also wingless, but in such cases the absence of wings is a secondary characteristic. That is to say, one acquired in the course of evolution as existing wings disappeared. This secondary wingless state is often found in insects which remain on the ground at all stages of development, and is apparent particularly in insects which live underground in cracks or caves. Many wingless insects are also found high up on mountains. Some populations include both winged and wingless members; in some species this depends on sex and it is usually the female which is wingless. Wings are an adult characteristic. Insects which undergo partial metamorphosis already have a rudimentary form of wings during the early stage of life when they are known as nymphs. With insects which undergo total metamorphosis the wings appear when the adult insect emerges from the pupa.

The insect abdomen is limbless, although in primitive orders it often has terminal appendages known as *cerci*. Larvae have appendages concerned with movement. For example, the legs of butterfly and sawfly larvae. The number of abdominal segments varies from a minimum of six, in Collembola, to a maximum of twelve in Protura.

We have said that insects do not have an internal skeleton; support is provided by the external skeleton, or exoskeleton, which also gives attachment to the muscles and thus makes

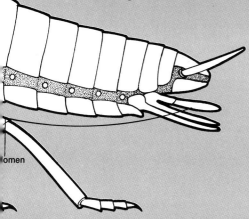

omen

movement possible. The cuticle, which forms the exoskeleton, has been found to consist of three layers, different in function and structure. The extremely thin outer layer makes the integument impermeable; the middle layer makes it rigid and hard; the inner layer is elastic and allows the joints to move. Chitin and sclerotin are the substances which give the structure the strength it needs; their presence is conditioned by the insect's habits and its related need for protection. The integument has to protect the insect against two main enemies: predators and excessive water loss. A strong leathery covering makes many insects unattractive to predators of a modest size, or even unassailable. Sedentary species in particular which cannot escape quickly benefit by this feature. The protection against water loss which the integument provides is often of fundamental importance. Hydrophilous insects which live in damp conditions have no special means of protection against dessication. Many species which live in caves or deep cracks in the ground, where there is plenty of moisture, die immediately of dehydration if removed from their surroundings.

The opposite is true of the so-called xerophilous species of insects, which like dry surroundings. For them water loss is an extremely grave problem requiring physiological or purely mechanical defence mechanisms. A tough, highly impermeable integument is often an indispensable condition for their survival.

The rigid external skeleton which serves for defence may hinder the animal's mobility. Some insects are so rigid that only very limited movement of their body segments in relation to one another is possible; this is true of many members of the Coleoptera, the armoured species in particular. However, the Coleoptera also include some very agile and articulated species. The abdomen of the Staphylinidae or Rove Beetles, for example, consists of segments which fit into one another, decreasing in size like the sections of a telescope so that the insect can move swiftly in all directions, even in narrow cracks. In other instances the most efficient joint is between two segments only and is related to a particular function. This is true of many sand beetles, in which a high degree of mobility between prothorax and mesothorax allows the animal to carry on its digging activity easily.

Finally, the integuments or 'skins' of insects have a variety of colourings and are often gaudily bright. The function of colour will be fully discussed later; the question here is how these colourings are achieved. The colour of insects may be chemical or physical in origin, and it may occur in the cuticle or beneath it. Chemical colour is due to the presence of certain pigments and while it may produce strong and even violent hues, it never gives metallic or iridiscent effects. Such splendid metallic lustres and iridescent sheens which come and go depending on how the light falls are a feature of many striking species and frequently appear in exotic fauna. They are caused by purely physical phenomena, as light catches on or is diffracted by thin lamellae or tiny subtly sculpted features. The location of colour pigment also varies. Insect collectors are only too familiar with an unwelcome but unavoidable phenomenon. The Dragonfly's splendid livery – black markings on a brilliant blue or fiery red ground – disappears within a few hours of the specimen's death, leaving a uniform brown. The same thing happens to the grass-green colour of many bugs, which turn straw-coloured as they dry out. This is because in these insects the cuticle is transparent and the colour pigment lies beneath it in the epidermis; as this dries out the colour will disappear.

**Mouth-parts**
Insects will eat anything, and for every type of organic material, whether it be fluid or solid, digestible or apparently indigestible, there will be some insect ready to make the most of it. Because of this range of diet the apparatus for the capture of food has in the course of evolution undergone a series of adaptations which have fundamentally changed the primitive structures.

▼ Diagrammatic section of the integument or 'skin'

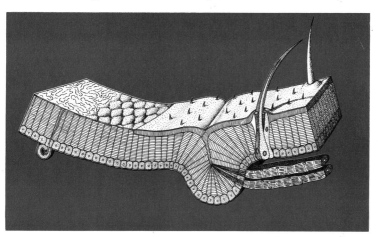

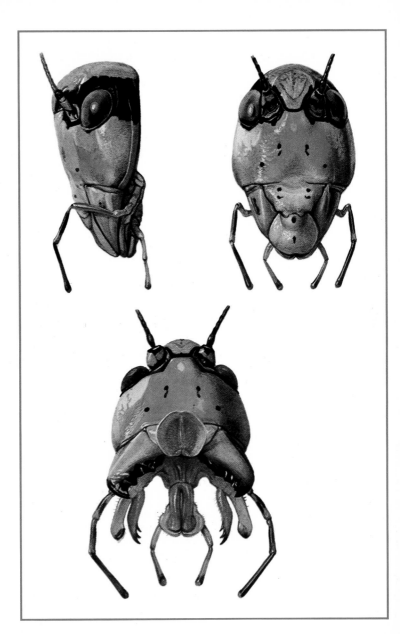

It is still easy to distinguish the constituents parts in the biting mouth parts of carnivorous and phytophagous (herbivorous) species. We can identify a labrum or upper lip, a pair of mandibles, a pair of jaws or maxillae with appendages known as maxillary palps, and a labium or lower lip with labial palps. These parts usually move in a horizontal plane. Carnivorous species are generally distinguished by long, thin mandibles, while those of herbivores are short and robust.

One of the most frequent modifications of the mouth parts is their transformation into a piercing and sucking organ. In Cicadas or bugs of the family Cimicidae, which feed on plant sap or animal blood, this modification particularly affects the mandibles and maxillae, which become stylets for piercing and

◀ Biting mouthparts in Orthoptera          ▼ Piercing mouthparts of Hemiptera

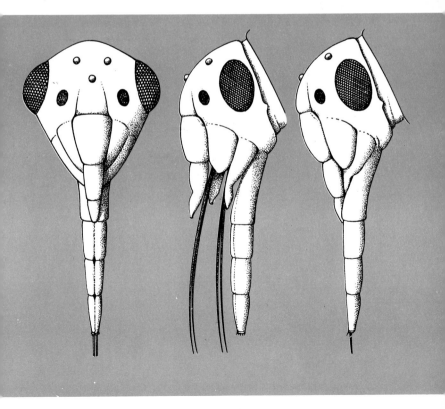

sucking, and the labium which encloses them in a kind of tube. This apparatus, known as the rostrum, may be long and slender or short and robust, depending on the feeding habits of the various species. In blood-sucking species of Diptera (such as Mosquitoes, Horseflies or Tsetse Flies) the mouth parts have a similar function, but the primitive parts are modified in a different way; all parts are lengthened, including the labrum or upper lip which comes to form a minute channel along which the liquid is sucked. In flies, the labium or lower lip is more developed, forming a short, broad-tipped proboscis. Flower-loving butterflies probe the corolla with a long proboscis which

▼ Mouthparts of Diptera

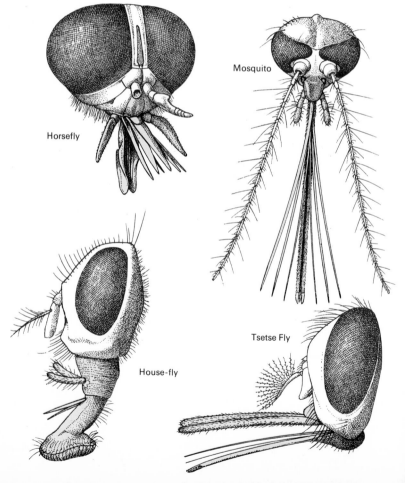

Horsefly

Mosquito

House-fly

Tsetse Fly

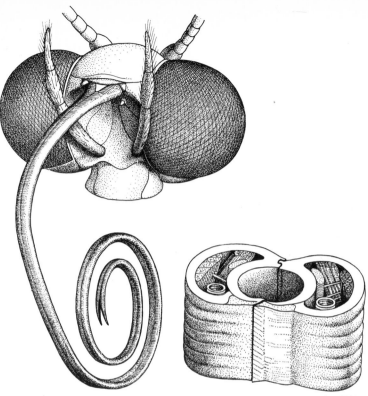

▲ Mouthparts of a butterfly

▼ Mouthparts of a bee

▲ In section

▼ In section

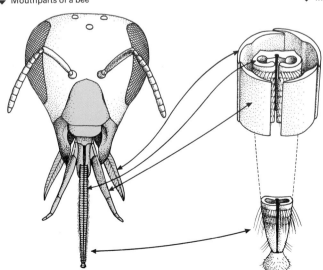

when not in use is coiled up beneath the insect's head. This organ is a modification of part of the maxillae. As a compromise, in bees the mandibles still have the function and primitive structure of a chewing organ, but the rest of the apparatus is lengthened to form a structure for licking and sucking the liquid sugary substances used to make honey.

### Antennae

The sensory apparatus of insects is complex. Antennae, the most obvious of the sense organs, are present in most insects, except the primitive soil-living Protura.

▼ Various types of Antennae

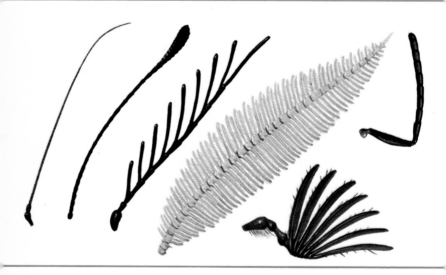

Insects have two antennae situated on the head near the compound eyes. They are concerned with the sense of smell and allow the insect to pick up scent. Antennae come in many shapes and sizes, consisting of a variable number of segments and a system of muscles, so that movement is possible.

In some groups of insects, all species have the same shape of antennae. With the Orthoptera, for example, they are filiform and slender, lengthened to some extent and often made up of a large number of segments. The antennae of aquatic insects like Stoneflies and Caddis Flies are similar.

However, the antennae often vary greatly in form, even among insects which are closely related. Among the Coleoptera there is a whole range of modifications, often bizarre and striking in effect. In Long-horn Beetles, for example, the antennae are exceptionally developed, often twice and sometimes four times the length of the body. Characteristic of the Scarabaeoidea are antennae which end in a kind of fan, formed by the expansion of the last segments, a feature which has earned them the name Lamellicornia. Weevils have the

▲ Long-horn Beetle

head prolonged into a rostrum or beak which carries a pair of antennae with the second segment (or scape) well developed: antennae of this type are described as elbowed or geniculate.

Other groups of insects add further variations to these odd features: pectinate antennae with branches like the teeth of a comb, clavate or club-shaped antennae and others with segments like a string of pearls, known as moniliform antennae.

29

Antennae structure is often linked to sex; it is usually the males which have the most developed and richly ornamented antennae. In male Mosquitoes, for example, they are feathery (or plumose), while in the female they are filiform. Similarly, in many species of moth, the male has bipectinate antennae which are far more ostentatious than the female's. They allow the male to locate a possible mate over amazing distances, sometimes more than seven miles, as has been observed in the case of *Actias selene*.

Sometimes the antennae are not just concerned with the senses. In some Springtails of the sub-order Symphypleona the male antennae have a kind of pincer with which the insect anchors itself to the antennae of the female which then carries it. The antennae of some Coleoptera of the family Meloidae have a similar function.

All insects have the problem of cleaning their antennae. Many have special organs on their front legs for this purpose. In Bees, their cleaning organs consists of a kind of notch formed by the metatarsus and a spur, or fibula.

▼ Pectinate antennae
of a Moth

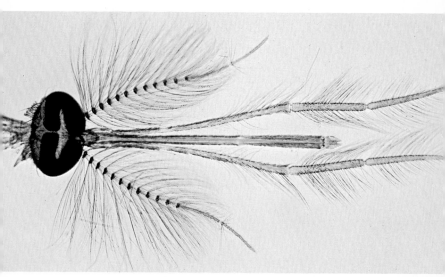

▲ Plumose antenna
of Mosquito

▼ Lamellate antennae
of Cockchafer

31

### Eyes

It is practically impossible for a human being to imagine the visual world of insects. Their eyes are quite different from ours in structure and function, and thus give a totally different view of the surrounding world. In the first place, insects have two different types of eyes: simple ocelli and compound eyes. The former consist of a single visual unit and in adults are situated at the back of the head. Their function is not clear, but they certainly do not supply a detailed image.

The compound eyes are more complex and functional: they

▼ Appearance of a flower, as seen by an insect

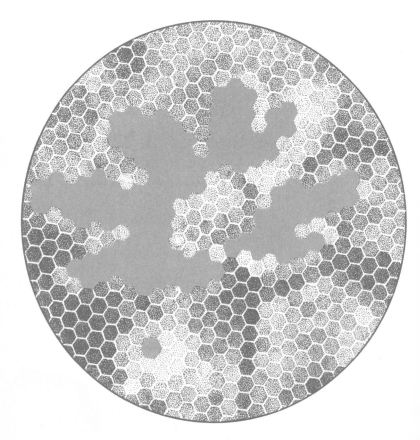

▼ Section of a compound eye

▼ Structure of one ommatidium

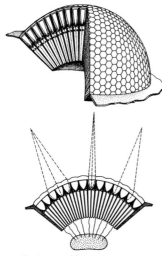

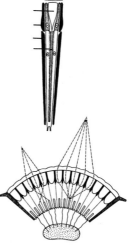

▲ Eye in apposition state

▲ Eye in superposition state

▲ Eye of a Dragonfly

33

consist of simple elements known as ommatidia which vary greatly in number. Externally, the eye appears as a more or less densely facetted surface. Under the microscope the individual facets are normally a regular hexagonal shape and each has its corresponding ommatidium. In section, the ommatidium is seen to consist of a cornea, a lens, pigment cells and the sensory part known as the retinula. The image which the insect sees is a combination of the images supplied by the individual ommatidia. However, this may happen in different ways. It may be that each retinula perceives the image from several ommatidia; the resulting superposition gives less sharp vision. An insect's sensitiveness to colours is very different from man's. They can see colours invisible to us. For example, ultraviolet, since they can perceive wavelengths outside man's visible spectrum. Some can even perceive the plane in which waves of polarized light vibrate.

▼ Eye of Horsefly

▼ Surface of the eye made up of ommatidia

▲ Eye of Stable Fly

There is a close link between life style and the effectiveness of an insect's vision. Species which live in dark surroundings often have relatively undeveloped eyes which scarcely protrude from the head and consist of only a limited number of ommatidia. Insects which live underground or in caves may have no eyes at all, as is the case with many parasites. On the other hand, some species have enormous eyes which take up much of the surface of the head. This is so with Dragonflies, predatory insects which have to catch their victims on the wing, and Horseflies which have enormous eyes, often of a brilliant metallic green with bronzed striations. Sight is often developed very differently in larva and adult; the life habits of many larvae are such that they do not need eyes, since they stay inside nests made beforehand by the adults, or inside the material which provides their food. The adult, on the other hand, needs eyes to find its food and mates of the opposite sex.

▼ Colour vision of Man

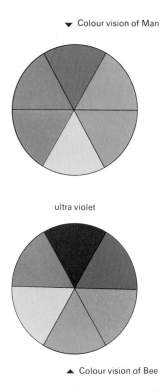

ultra violet

▲ Colour vision of Bee

## Legs

As a rule, insects have three pairs of legs, one for each segment of the thorax. This regular feature of all members of the Class has given insects their other name, Hexapoda.

The typical insect leg consist of five main segments. The first, the coxa, articulates with the body; then comes the trochanter, which is usually small; the third segment, the femur, is the sturdiest and has a strong muscular system; the fourth, the tibia, is usually long and slender, but robust. The last part is made up of a variable number of joints known as tarsi, and often ends in a pair of hooked appendages.

The main function of insect legs is, of course, locomotion. However, each insect has its own way of moving and this conditions the shape, size and muscles of its limbs. The typical structure is that of the ground or plant-living insects. The tarsus provides a fulcrum, and the rest moves by the lever principle. The legs of water insects and jumping insects are modified; they are paddle-like in the former and have a powerful musculature in the latter. The most obvious transformations occur when the leg serves some function other than movement. In Mantids, for example, the front legs have

▼ Types of legs

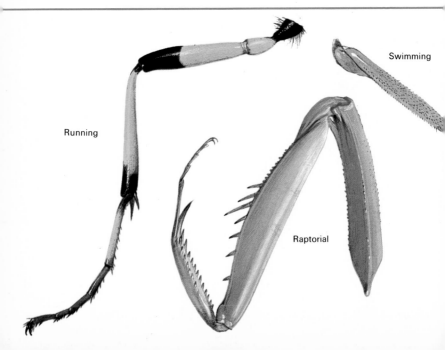

Running

Swimming

Raptorial

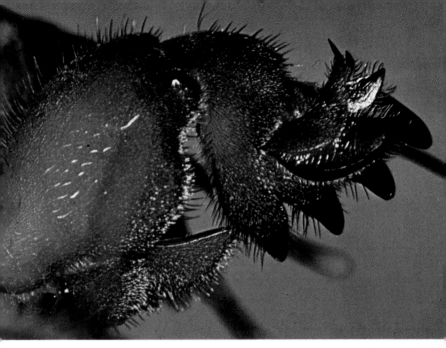

▲ Fore leg of a Mole Cricket

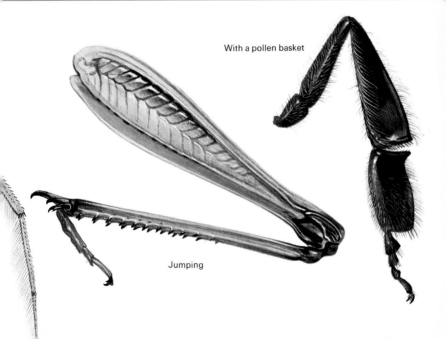

With a pollen basket

Jumping

become instruments of capture (raptorial): the coxa is highly developed, and the tibia and tarsi form hooks, so that the legs can shoot out and seize the victim. In the Mole-cricket, the modification is even more fundamental and obvious, so that the insect can burrow into the ground. The front leg acts as both shovel and shears; it is extremely strong, is provided with teeth, and is capable of a movement between tibia and tarsus which can slice through any roots in the insect's way. Insect legs often have secondary functions in addition to movement. Many species have special structures on the front legs for cleaning the delicate and important antennae. In Bees and other honey producing members of the Hymenoptera the hind legs are equipped with a special hollow known as a pollen basket in which the animal keeps the collected pollen to feed the larvae. In many species of Grasshopper the hind legs produce sounds made by rubbing the femur against the wing. Certain species of Grasshopper have their hearing organs in their front legs. With many insects the larvae moves quite differently from the adult. With insects which undergo total metamorphosis the larvae are often apodal or legless, or else have short limbs unsuitable for walking. On the other hand, in addition to their real legs, larvae often have appendages, prolegs, which assist movement but which are temporary features absent in the adult insect. The caterpillars of Butterflies and Sawflies have from two to five pairs of prolegs, since the real legs are too far forward and on their own too weak for easy movement. In caterpillars of the Moth family,

▼ Caterpillar, showing pseudolegs

▲ Tarsal claws of a Stag-beetle

Geometridae, the two pairs of prolegs make a very special kind of 'looping' movement possible. The animal holds on with its front legs, lifts the prolegs, arches its body, and draws them up close to the front legs.

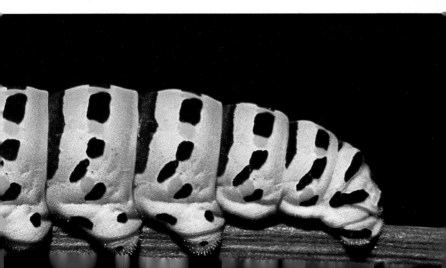

## Wings

It has already been said that insects are the only invertebrates
which can fly and therefore their wings are an organ not found
in other invertebrate animals. It is useful to compare the insect
wing with that of other animals capable of active flight as
opposed to mere gliding – birds and bats. In both, the wing is
simply a modification of the forelimb, providing a large surface
area composed of remiges or large feathers in the case of birds,
and of a large wing-membrane or patagium in the case of bats.
In other words, in order to fly these animals lose the walking
function of one pair of limbs. Insects, however, have nothing to

▼ Wings of Insects

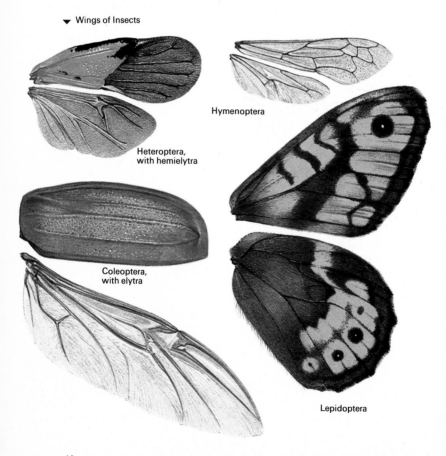

Heteroptera,
with hemielytra

Hymenoptera

Coleoptera,
with elytra

Lepidoptera

lose; the wing is not a modified limb, but a layered structure derived from expansions which had a primitive gliding function and then became able to move by means of the thoracic muscles. The insect wing consists of two superimposed, usually thin, layers, criss-crossed, a framework of veins which can vary enormously. These 'veins' are thickened tubes which strengthen the wing as a whole, and which are supplied with tracheae, nerves and lymph. Wing venation is often highly complex in so-called primitive insects such as Dragonflies, forming a close network on the wing. In more advanced insects, particularly small ones, the venation may be much

▼ Scarce
Swallowtail Butterfly

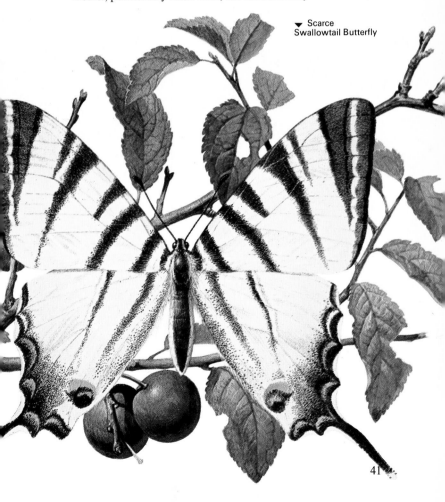

▲ Thrip

▲ Plume Moth

▲ Halteres of Tipulid

simpler and often only the costal vein which forms the anterior border of the wing is well developed. The system of names used to differentiate the veins is complex, as is only to be expected, since wing venation is often an important characteristic for identifying species.

Insects usually have four wings, carried on the second and third thoracic segments. Their development and shape vary enormously in the different orders. Membranous transparent wings are the most frequent and occur in all primitive types found near water (Dragonflies, Mayflies, Stoneflies), and in many species of Diptera (Flies and Mosquitoes) and

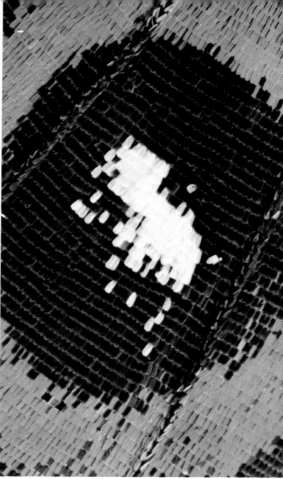

Scales on wing of a Butterfly ▲

Hymenoptera (Bees and Wasps). Often, however, only the hind wings are membranous and transparent, while the forewings become thick and tough to serve as protection for the second pair of wings and the abdomen. The phenomenon can just be seen in the Orthoptera (Grasshoppers and Crickets) in which the front pair of wings are known as tegmina. The feature takes a curious form in bugs, Heteroptera, in which the forewings (or hemielytra) are only partially hardened. It is most apparent in Coleoptera where the forewings, known as elytra, have a purely protective function, forming a tough shield which covers the soft back of the abdomen; they play no active part in flight.

43

▲ Elytra and membranous wing of a Cockchafer

This transformation also affects the membranous wings which are usually longer than the elytra; to remain covered when at rest they fold along a kind of hinge.

The characteristic feature of Butterfly and Moth wings is their colouring – often bright and sometimes mimetic. The wings of these insects would be transparent, without the numerous coloured scales which cover them, and give the typical, multi-coloured designs. The males also have a special form of scales on their wings which discharge scent to attract the opposite sex. Small Moths of the family Pterophoridae have a very special type of wings, divided into slender branches

▲ Pair of Crickets

with feathery fringes to bear the insect in flight.

As has been shown, the forewings of Coleoptera have lost their function of supporting the insect in flight, and similar phenomena occur in many other groups of insect. Flies and Mosquitoes belong to the order Diptera, a name which indicates that these insects only have two wings. In fact, even Diptera have four wings, but the second pair is so reduced that the word 'wing' does not really apply. Instead we find a small organ with no flying function which acts as a static sense organ or balancer, and is known as a haltere. In Flies, it is in the form of a small squama; in Mosquitoes heart-shaped.

45

### Internal structure

All animals have in common a number of vital mechanisms.
Feeding, breathing, the elimination of waste products, the
reception of stimuli from the outside world and
reproduction are the particular functions of animal life
which occur in any animal group. However, the ways in
which these functions are performed are extremely varied,
since each group solves the problem in its own way. In this
respect, insects are among the most successful of animals,
since their natural organs are developed in a highly

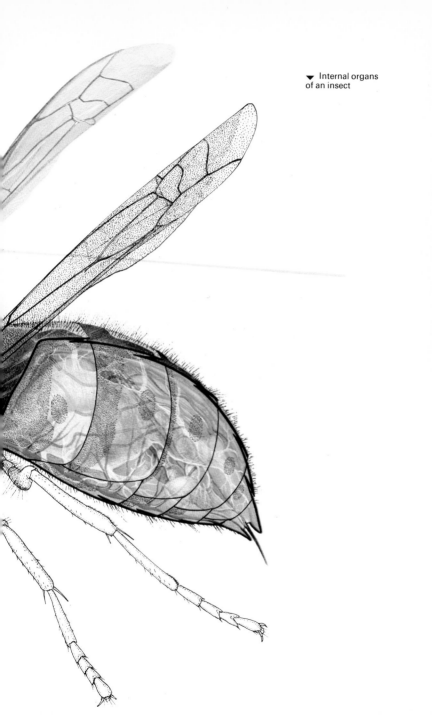

▼ Internal organs
of an insect

functional way. Their organs are totally different from those of vertebrates, and it is very interesting to compare the different solutions adopted by the two groups, bearing in mind the different problem they face, not least those posed by the great disparity of size. The different solutions for the capture of food, through modifications of the mouth apparatus, have already been discussed. Obviously the digestive apparatus too has to be adapted to the feeding habits of different species. The digestive canal is divided into three parts: the fore, mid and hind gut. Formed differently in the course of embryonic development, these three sections also have different functions. The fore gut, for example, often contains salivary glands which produce secretions for such specific purposes as preventing the coagulation of blood swallowed by blood-sucking insects. In species which feed on very tough materials the part known as the gizzard may be particularly developed, with thickened walls to continue the grinding-up of the food begun in the mouth. A special characteristic of insects is the presence in the mid gut of the so called peritrophic membrane which encloses the food as it passes along the digestive canal and is normally expelled with the faeces.

The presence of a circulatory apparatus is not a constant feature in all animals, but depends on the organism's requirements in carrying nourishment to, and waste from, each part of the body. Very small animals can do without a circulatory apparatus. Insects are large enough to encounter problems and so have a circulatory fluid called blood, or, more properly haemolymph, pumped by the heart. There is a basic difference between insect and vertebrate circulation. In vertebrates the blood flows along well-defined vessels – arteries and veins ending in capillaries – constituting a 'closed' system of circulation. In insects, the blood flows freely in the body, not contained in vessels. The only place where the haemolymph passes along a vessel is in the heart, which is a tubular dorsal organ divided by septa: the blood enters through valves and is then propelled by contractions of the muscles which make up the heart. The flow of this blood, haemolymph, is generally towards the head.

Insect blood is a variety of colours, often yellow or green, but, significantly, almost never red. The red colour of so many animals' blood is due to the presence of a pigment, haemoglobin, which carries oxygen from the animal's respiratory organs to its tissues. In land insects the method of respiration is developed in a particular way which makes respiratory pigment unnecessary. On the sides of the insect's body there are holes known as spiracles, or stigmata, which open and close. These openings lead to the tracheae, tiny tubes along which the air passes. After branching out each trachea ends in a special cell. Then they subdivide into numerous branches known as tracheoles which lead directly to the tissues where the oxygen is used for cellular respiration. This explains why insects can do without respiratory pigment; it is not needed because the oxygen reaches the tissues directly, without intermediary stages. The tracheal system has other clear advantages, besides making respiratory pigment unnecessary. It allows for an interchange of gases at a speed which would be out of the question for organisms in which oxygen reaches the cells by means of the blood. This makes exceptional muscular activity possible, as for example with insects which can stay immobile in the air for a considerable time. However the larvae of aquatic species of Diptera belonging to the family of Chironomidae do contain haemoglobin, an exception explained by the animal's surroundings. These larvae live in stagnant water and thrive even in putrid water containing little oxygen. Since they have gills instead of the tracheae of land insects, and so lack their direct air supply, these larvae need oxygen-carrying pigment in order to breathe in their suffocating surroundings. Many other aquatic larvae, it should be noted, have gills and tracheal gills instead of tracheae.

Another problem for all animal species is the elimination of waste material. Whatever method the organism adopts to break down organic matter and extract the energy it needs, in the end it is always left with useless or even harmful substances. This so-called katabolic material has to be eliminated by the process known as excretion. In mammals and other vertebrates this function is, of course, performed by the kidneys. In insects the excretory organs are the Nalphigian tubes which are attached to the end of the intestine. They discharge waste products into the intestine, together with a greater amount of water than the animal could safely eliminate; this water is then re-absorbed by the intestinal wall. On the whole the operation is the same as occurs in the kidneys of a mammal, although performed by a quite different organ. Insects also have another ingenious and useful way of eliminating waste. They store waste material in the cuticle.

Periodically, when it has to abandon its too-small covering in order to grow, an insect gets rid of the waste material together with its old skin.

The nervous system of insects differs fundamentally in two ways from the vertebrate system with which nearly everyone is generally familiar. Above all, it is not fully centralized like the vertebrate system. There is a brain situated in the head above the first tract of the digestive canal, but below the canal there is another important nerve centre known as the suboesophageal ganglion which controls the movement of the mouth-parts. These two nerve centres are linked by the circumesophageal connective and a ventral nerve cord. A succession of ganglia linked by the nerve cord continues along the animal's ventral side, rather than along its back, and this is the second way in which the system differs from that of vertebrates. Originally there was one ganglion to each body segment, but in the course of evolution several ganglia have fused into one, as for example in Diptera where the three thoracic ganglia have combined to form one.

Insect reproduction usually involves separate sexes; that is to

▼ Diagram of circulation in an Insect

▼ Diagram of circulation in Vertebrates

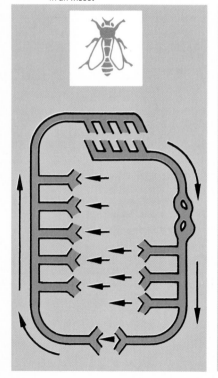

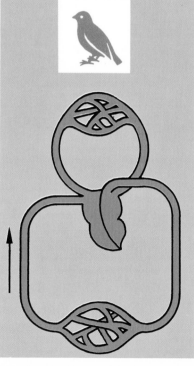

say it occurs by the mating of individuals, the female which bears the egg cell and the male which produces spermatozoa. The female organs consist of two ovaries linked by a common oviduct, a vagina for the actual mating, and, usually, a spermatheca which is a pouch, often sclerotized, where the sperm is stored after mating. The male has two testes linked by spermatic ducts to a single canal which ends in the copulatory organ or adeagus. The form of the adeagus is extremely varied even within closely related groups of species, and so provides the entomologist concerned with classification with a useful characteristic for differentiating between species which are very close in external structure. It also makes it possible to reconstruct the evolutionary stages which have produced existing species, and, beside distinguishing similar insects, helps to show resemblances between different forms.

▼ Spiracle with trachea

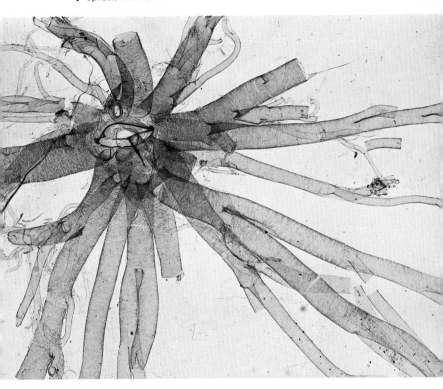

51

# Growth and Reproduction

As already mentioned, the new-born insect which hatches from the egg is often very different from the mature individual capable of reproduction, and there may be differences of form, function and habitat. In general, it can be said that the adult is more capable of movement than the larvae, but with a smaller capacity for consuming food. The adult insect usually has a far shorter life-span.

When the animal reaches sexual maturity it does not grow any more and so dqes not moult again.

The differences between larvae and adults are far more pronounced in the groups of insect considered to be more

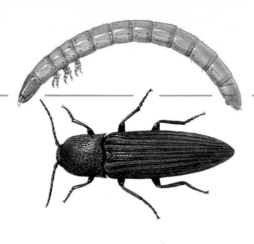

evolved; they correspond to a fundamental division of labour in these species between the larvae and adult stages, so that often the young insect in effect limits itself to eating, the adult to reproduction.

The existence of a larval stage is a widespread feature of invertebrates, in no way confined to insects alone. However, in insects, which are pre-eminently land animals, the adult has a function which in aquatic invertebrates is usually the pre-rogative of the larvae: the dispersal of the species over the largest possible area in order to avoid over-crowding and to colonize all areas suitable for the needs of that particular species.

In marine invertebrates, the larvae, generally borne by current, cover remarkable distances in the vast drifts of animal life known as plankton.

It is possible to speak of a plankton of the air. Many insects capable of flight but not really able to move independently of air currents let themselves be carried for enormous distances. This only applies to adult insects, as they alone have wings which can keep them up in flight. In many species the movement and dispersal of adults is a completely active process, since these insects have strong functional wings and so are not governed by air movements and can even fly against the wind, guided by their own sense of smell.

The series of transformations which take place in the course of the insect's life are called metamorphosis, and we shall examine the main types known to occur.

The most primitive insects are wingless as adults. Called Apterygota from the Greek meaning 'without wings', their development is usually fairly simple and, apart from reaching sexual maturity, the insect does not acquire special organs during the life. True metamorphosis is generally considered to be absent in these Apterygotes, which are classed as ametabolous.

In the enormous group of insect classed as hemimatabola, it is characteristic for the young forms to be very similar to the adults. The most obvious difference is the absence of wings, which appear gradually. They are completely lacking in the earliest stage, but appear as short stumps in the next stages which are known as nymphs. They only become functional after the last moult. There are many variations on this basic pattern.

How similar the early stages and the adults are depends on whether they live in the same environment. Ephemeroptera, Odonata and Plecoptera develop in water and so obviously need special structures. For example, the tracheal system of respiration would not work, and so is replaced by tracheal gills; these sometimes grow from the sides of the abdomen like little frills, and are sometimes leaf-shaped appendages at the end of the abdomen. Ephemeroptera have a unique characteristic among insects. After leaving the water and acquiring wings they undergo a further moult, abandoning the old integument even in their winged state; this type of metamorphosis is described as prometabolous and the winged insect, which moults again, is called the sub-imago. The mouth parts of Odonata or Dragonfly nymphs which are modified in a unique way will be described later.

In other hemimetabolous insects the difference is usually less.

Young Grasshoppers, Mantids, Cockroaches and Bugs are very similar to the adults. Sometimes they may even appear to be ametabolous, when the adult is in fact a secondarily wingless insect.

Complete metamorphosis is a characteristic method of insect growth. The process, which occurs in the more evolved orders, as a rule goes through four stages. First comes the egg. Then follows the larval stage, during which the insect leads an active life, usually confining itself to eating and increasing its volume. After a certain number of months, each accompanied by growth in size and tiny structural modifications, the animal enters a quiescent stage. It remains immobile, covered by a rigid integument and often encased in a cocoon prepared by the larvae. During this resting stage, or pupa, the animal undergoes drastic internal and external transformations which turn it into an adult. Among the most important transformations are the formation of wings and the reaching of sexual maturity. The length of the complete growth cycle varies enormously. Generally speaking, the larvae live much longer than the adults, as for example with the Stag-beetle which chews away at oak stumps for five years as larva to live for only a few weeks as an adult. However, the larval period may be much briefer, since many species have several generations during a single year. The phases of the growth cycle are conditioned by the course of the seasons. The insect may survive through the winter as egg or pupa, or as larva or adult depending on the species and on environment.

Larvae and adults, as has been said, often live quite differently. The larva, as a voracious eater, spends its life inside its food, whether it be wood, rotten meat or dung; generally the food is not very nourishing and can be consumed in large quantities. The adult usually eats little and often finds in flowers what little nectar or pollen it requires.

The varied life habits of larvae have produced a whole range of modifications and environmental adaptations. Sedentary larvae, which live inside their food, are often legless or have very reduced legs. The mouth parts are the organism's only strong structure.

The larvae of many Flies and Blowflies are also legless, but they tackle their feeding problems not with the help of strong mandibles but by absorbing food which is already partly digested. They do not have a proper head, but the mouth parts end in a pair of hooks: special secretions make the food liquid so that the insects can consume it without any positive chewing at all.

## Hormonal Control

The growth and metamorphosis of insects are controlled by an endocrine system and so ultimately depend on hormones. The endocrine system in turn is closely linked to the brain which, as in vertebrates, exercise control over hormone production. The growth hormone, ecdysone, is produced by a gland in the thorax known as the prothoracic gland: its function is to stimulate growth and moulting. This gland functions closely with the *corpora allata*, endocrine glands close to the brain. They produce the juvenile hormone which involves the maintenance of the larval structures. If enough of this juvenile hormone circulates in the insect's blood, the moult stimulated by the ecdysone leads to the formation of a new larval stage; when the amount falls below a certain level the pupa stage follows the moult; in the absence of the juvenile hormone the transition from pupa to adult occurs.

Although the patterns of growth so far described are generally found in most insect orders, there are some intermediate forms and exceptions.

The development of Thysanoptera or Thrips, for example, small plant-living animals, falls roughly between that of hemimetabolous and holometabolous insects (those undergoing complete metamorphosis). These insects pass through two resting stages before becoming adults. Other types of life cycle are fairly frequent. The alternation of generations in many species of Homoptera will be dealt with at length later, so here it is only necessary to mention that in some species the mother gives birth to small ready-formed larvae instead of eggs. Although the larvae of holometabolous insects are generally very different from the adults, female Glow Worms closely resemble larvae, while the male have all the characteristics of adult Coleoptera. Finally, there is the exceptional case of larvae which generate more larvae directly, a phenomenon known as paedogenesis which occurs in several genera of dipterous gall-midges.

In the early stage insects sometimes live in isolation, but they often tend to live in groups, whether because they can hardly move at all and so cannot get far from the spot where the mother has laid the eggs, which will in any case be close to food or even inside it, or because they actually have gregarious tendencies. A case in point are the Processionary Moths which as caterpillars live in nests built by a great number of individuals and actually move in procession when they leave their refuge to seek food. Generally speaking, a single nymph or larva hatches from each insect egg.

Stages of hemimetabola (1), pseudometabola (2), holometabola (3) ▶

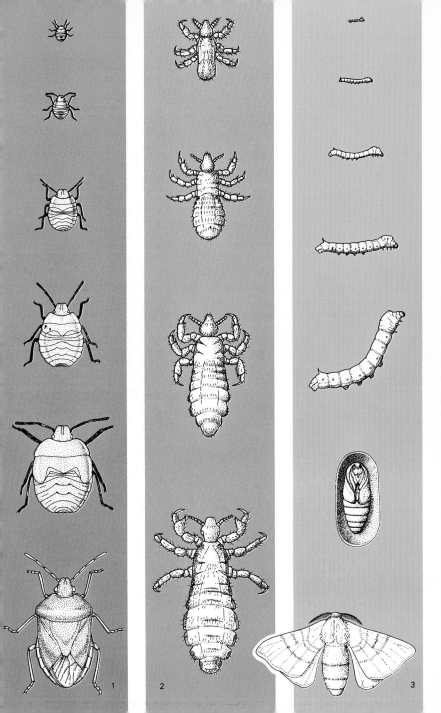

▲ Aquatic stage of a Dragonfly

▲ The adult Dragonfly

▼ Stages in the life of a Cabbage Butterfly

## Metamorphosis

After the general account of the stages of metamorphosis in earlier pages, it is worth examining some typical examples.

Dragonflies lead an amphibious life. The larvae, or rather nymphs, live in water and feed on small animals. The adult is also carnivorous, but it is a flying hunter which catches its prey as it hovers over the water.

The Cabbage White Butterfly of the family Pieridiae lays its eggs on cruciferous plants. A characteristic of this insect is the way the pupa attaches itself to its support with fine silk thread. The life history of the House-fly, a holometabolous insect like

▼ Life cycle of a House-fly

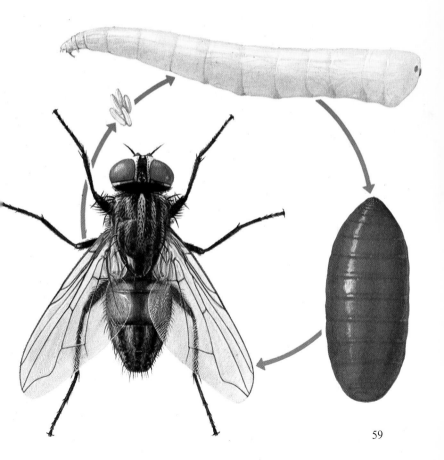

59

the Cabbage White, follows the same pattern as the Butterfly's. However, the larva has no real head; a tapering sausage-shape and is legless, it has tracheal spiracles at the tail end. This unusual arrangement of the breathing pores is explained by the habits of these larvae. They live in decomposing matter which they make liquid by means of special secretions; they thus live in a semi-liquid environment from which only the tip of the abdomen emerges.

The Cabbage White Butterfly chrysalis has bumps and ridges which correspond to the new organs which are being formed. However, the brown sheath inside which a fly completes its transformation is a segmented, barrel-shaped and relatively smooth case, known as the puparium.

### Eggs

Round or flat, long or barrel-shaped, crested or sculptured, insect eggs show an amazing range of shapes, sizes and colours. The shell which protects the embryo, called the chorion, is tough but not airproof. The embryo which develops inside it takes a varying amount of time to reach maturity, depending on environment. Many insects pass the winter in the egg stage.

The nutritive matter lies at the centre of the egg, while the

▼ Insect eggs

A Ladybird laying eggs ▶

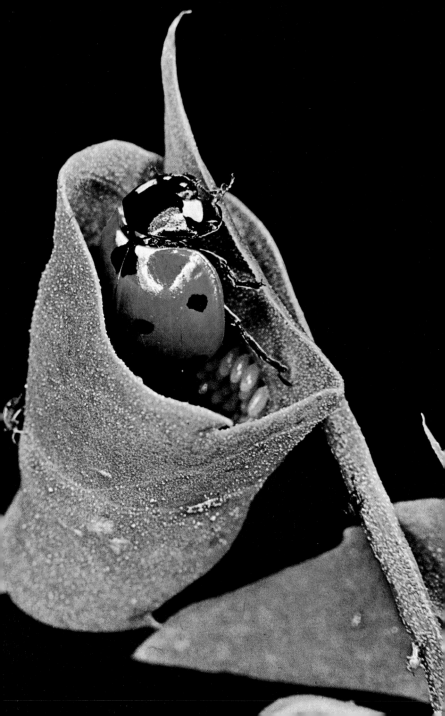

new insect develops on the periphery, and as the embryo develops it often makes characteristic movements. The problem posed of emerging from the egg should not be ignored; the tough chorion presents a considerable obstacle to the delicate, newly-formed individual, but this is often overcome by means of a special organ called the hatching spines which has the sole function of piercing the shell and is lost at the first moult.

Eggs are rarely laid in isolation; in fact this generally occurs only with species which build nests. Usually the eggs are systematically laid in groups.

▼ Ootheca (egg cases)

Mantid

Cockroach

Egg cluster of
*Lymantria* moth

### The Ootheca

Many species of insects do not like leaving their eggs unprotected and exposed to danger, or cannot build successful nests to store food for the new generation. To protect their eggs they produce oothecae – egg cases of various types and shapes. If you lift up a large stone in some sunny spot in warm countries you may well find in the space beneath long furrowed masses of a characteristic spongy material. These are the oothecae of a Mantid, made by the female with special glands which produce a thick liquid pumped from the end of the

▲ Egg laying by a Grasshopper

abdomen to dry as this spongy material. Mantids produce their oothecae on any suitable surface, not just under stones.

The oothecae of Cockroaches are smooth and tough, brown in colour with a serrated crest running lengthwise; the female carries them for some times at the end of her abdomen. Many Moths provide special protection for their eggs, by covering them with hairs from the tip of the abdomen. Many Grasshoppers entrust their eggs to the ground; they plunge the abdomen into the soil and by mixing earth with the secretion of special glands build a kind of muff in which the eggs are laid.

▲ Mayfly nymph

## Nymphs

As has been explained, the early stages of hemimetabolous insects (that is those undergoing partial metamorphosis) may or may not have a rudimentary form of wings. Dragonfly nymphs are among the most interesting. They are aquatic nymphs which sometimes have two clearly visible, narrow leaf-shaped tracheal gills at the end of the abdomen; these are present in members of the sub-order zygoptera (the so-called Damsel Flies) but absent in the Anisoptera (or true Dragonflies). Their mouth parts are undoubtedly their most characteristic feature: the highly developed lower lip, known in

▼ Mask of a Dragonfly nymph

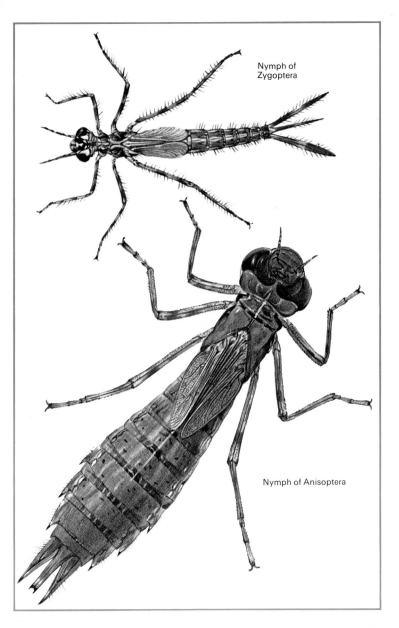

Nymph of Zygoptera

Nymph of Anisoptera

this case as a mask, is divided into two hinged laminae. When not in use the two component parts are folded under the head. When the nymph sights its prey – a larvae, a tadpole or even a small fish – it shoots out the mask and seizes its victim in the claws.

The nymphs of many species of Plecoptera or Stoneflies have a characteristic flattened shape, due to the micro-environment in which they live – they can be found under stones in running water, even where the current is strong. Living under stones in this way prevents them being carried away by the water, makes it easy for them to find food and also provides protection against possible enemies.

Hemimetabolous insects usually take less care over their offspring than the more evolved holometabolous insects which undergo complete metamorphosis. At most their attentions usually consist of the provision of oothecae, with none of the complex procedures found in Hymenoptera and Coleoptera.

In the attics of old houses you may find a kind of insect covered with fluff. This is the nymph of *Reduvius personatus*, a species of Assassin Bug.

▼ Newly-hatched Heteroptera       ▼ Nymphs of Heteroptera

▲ Grasshopper moulting

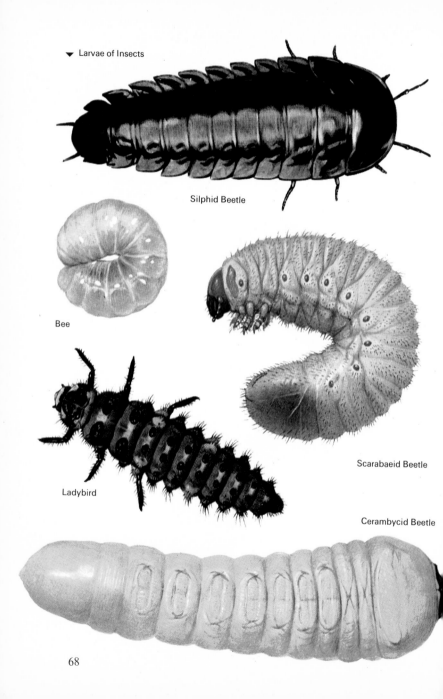

▼ Larvae of Insects

Silphid Beetle

Bee

Scarabaeid Beetle

Ladybird

Cerambycid Beetle

68

Staphylinid Beetle

Chironomid larva

Rat-tailed Maggot

**The Larva**
The illustrations on these pages readily show the wide range of
forms assumed by the larvae of insects which undergo total
metamorphosis. The larvae also try hard not to be seen, by
sheltering inside cases of coverings, a habit found in the larvae
of both land and aquatic insects. Among land species, the
caterpillars of many Butterflies and Moths are particularly
interesting. In the family Psychidae, the females do not leave
their cases, even as adults. Among aquatic species, the
Trichoptera or Caddis Fly larvae make pretty cases from a
whole range of materials – fragments of plants, pebbles and
tiny empty shells. Often a less attractive type of material is used
to protect and camouflage the case: many larvae habitually
cover themselves with their own excrement. This occurs with,
for example, the Lily Beetle of the family Chrysomelidae,
which can easily be found with the bright red adult on the
stalks of lilies and other plants of the same family. The larvae
of Tortoise Beetles (*Cassida*), besides covering themselves with
excrement, keep their exuviae at the end of their abdomen,
again to conceal themselves. Larvae of Tenthredinidae,
Sawflies, cover themselves with a dark, sticky secretion so that
they resemble little snails.

69

▲ Swallowtail larva showing osmaterium          Caterpillar of a Noctuid Moth ▶

A brief general look at insect larvae and their main characteristics would be appropriate at this point.

The larvae of Neuroptera are mainly predatory. The mouth parts of some species are interestingly developed to form a sucking organ, as for example in the larvae of the European Ant-lion or those of the Lacewing family Chrysopidae. The organ appears to consist of two long curved claws which are, in fact, the mandibles and maxillae together. They are hollow inside and the juices of the prey pass along them.

**GROWTH AND REPRODUCTION**

The special covering of the Caddis Fly larvae has already been described; in addition these larvae have tracheal gills instead of tracheae because of their aquatic habits.

Butterfly and Moth larvae, or caterpillars, usually live on the green parts of plants. Besides their abdominal prolegs, they sometimes have special appendages such as the osmeterium of the Papilionidae (a forked organ near the head, which the animal raises if disturbed), the abdominal filaments of the Puss Moth (*Cerura*), or the horn of the Hawk Moth (family Sphingidae).

The larvae of Diptera are very varied and include both forms, those with a distinct head and those headless sausage-like more typical fly larvae. Habits vary correspondingly. In addition to the many species which favour decomposing matter and stagnant water, there are carnivorous, plant-feeding and parasite forms. The Mosquito larvae which lives in stagnant water but breathes atmospheric oxygen has its own solution to the problem of respiration: it is equipped with an abdominal syphon with which it pierces the surface film of the water from below; it therefore always has to live at the surface.

Hymenoptera are the order of insects which take greatest care of their offspring. Often their larvae cannot move. Only the larvae of plant-eating species are left to manage as best they can, like butterfly and mother caterpillars they often have prolegs. Terebrantia lay their eggs inside the bodies of other insects. The Aculeata are the most painstaking, building nests of different materials to store supplies for the larvae.

▼ Mosquito larvae

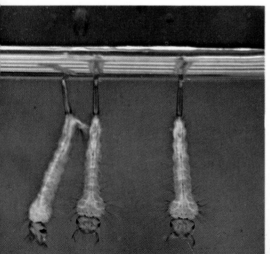

In general, as has been said, the larvae of holometabolous insects change little in form as they develop, but simply grow in size. Sometimes, however, the same species goes through different larvae forms, alternating with resting periods similar to the pupa stage. This phenomenon, hypermetamorphosis, occurs in parasitic species. The hypermetamorphic life cycle of the beetle family Meloidae is well known. These are medium-sized insects which as adults are often red and black or metallic green in colour: this green colouring is typical of *Lytta vesicatoria* (Spanish-fly or Blister Beetle), a beetle well known for the blistering substances called cantharadin which it contains. A typical member of the family is the *Meloe* or Oil-beetle, a large black beetle which has a short elytra and does not have operative wings for flight. But to return to the life-cycle: the larva which hatches from the egg is very mobile and has three claws to each tarsus which is hence described as triungulin. It climbs to a flower of a type frequented by solitary bees and then lets itself be carried by a bee to the inside of its nest. It now changes into the second type of larva and feeds on the honey which the bee has stored. When it reaches a certain size it enters a stage similar to a pupa. However, from this stage it emerges not as an adult but as a new larva which then becomes the real pupa from which the adult finally emerges.

▼ Larva and adult of an Oil Beetle

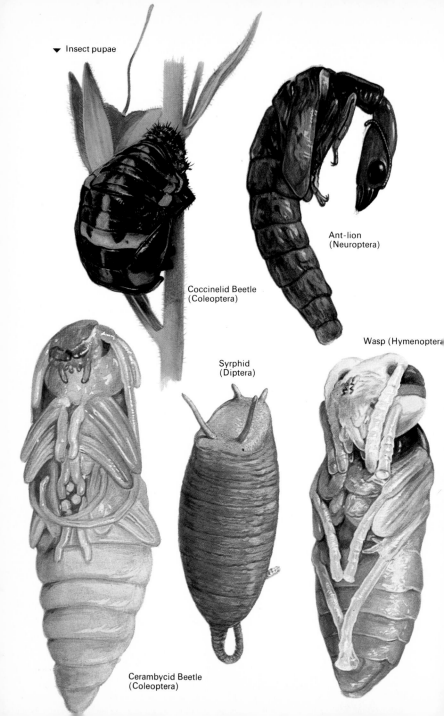

Insect pupae

Coccinelid Beetle
(Coleoptera)

Ant-lion
(Neuroptera)

Wasp (Hymenoptera)

Syrphid
(Diptera)

Cerambycid Beetle
(Coleoptera)

## The Pupa

During the pupa stage the organisation of the holometabolous insect, immobile in its rigid case, undergoes a drastic transformation. Old organs disappear, new ones take shape. At the beginning of this stage the insect usually has a pale translucent and opalescent appearance. Gradually, starting from fixed points, it becomes darker until it is the same colour as the adult. Usually, during this transitional period, the insect makes itself some form of shelter, cocoon or cell, since it is incapable of movement and so it is exposed to attack from predators and parasites. To build a cell it gathers round itself whatever material is available. The cocoon, however, is a feature of species with silk-producing glands. The pupae of holometabolous insects fall into two types, described as obtect, when the integument encloses the whole insect, and as exarate when some or all of the appendages are free.

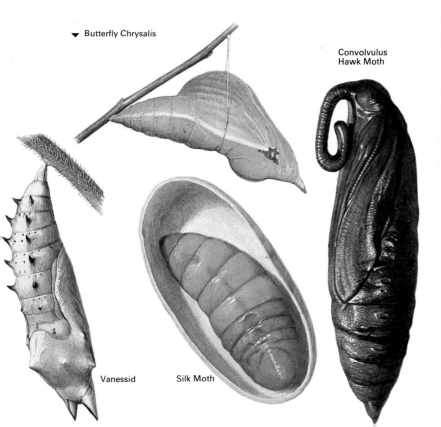

▼ Butterfly Chrysalis

Convolvulus
Hawk Moth

Vanessid

Silk Moth

## Mating

The majority of insect species have two sexes. Reproductive activity, therefore, involves finding a partner and mating. It is usually the male which actively looks for a mate, relying on a whole range of signals emitted by the female, such as odour, which is one of the commonest methods of sexual attraction. The large feathery antennae of many moths are used to detect the special odours emitted by the female. The light signals and sounds which many insects produce also play their part in sexual attraction.

Once the male and female have met, mating takes place in a number of ways. In Thysanura and Collembola no actual coupling occurs. The male deposits small masses of spermatic material known as spermatophores, carried by a peduncle, which are left to be picked up by the female. Many other primitive insects produce spermatophores, but they are placed directly in the female genitals during coupling. Coupling methods are varied, depending on the structure of the insect's body and copulatory organs. The way in which the female mantid brutally devours the male after coupling is in contrast to the curiously attractive spectacle of the male and female Dragonfly linked to form a heart shape. This position is necessary because the male reproductive organs are at the base of the abdomen, not its tip.

▼ Syrphids mating

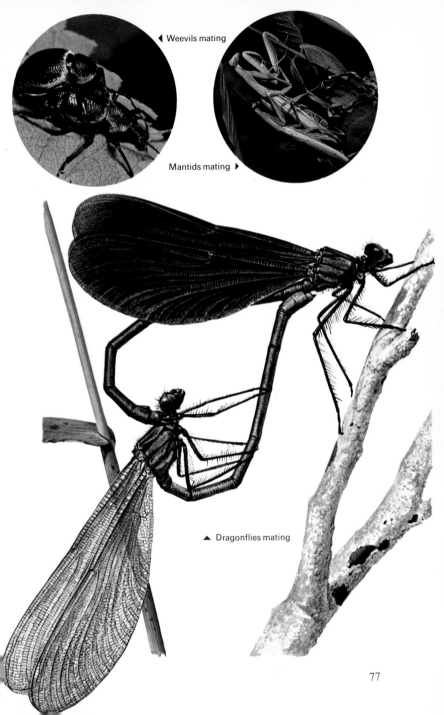

◀ Weevils mating

Mantids mating ▶

▲ Dragonflies mating

77

## Care of the Offspring

As with all animals the most difficult moment of the insect's existence is when it has just emerged form the egg. The tiny, defenceless new-born creature is exposed to the attack of countless enemies. The mother obviously has to take care to lay the eggs in a sheltered spot, preferably in direct contact with food. Egg laying, therefore, requires special organs, adapted to the offspring's requirements. The females of many insects have

▼ Abdominal segments used as a substitute ovipositor in Diptera.

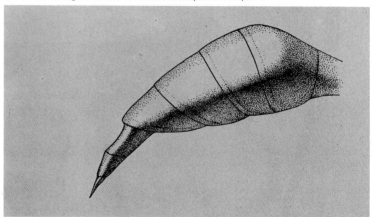

▼ Ovipositor of Sawfly (Hymenoptera)

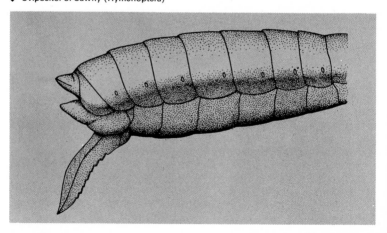

an abdominal appendage, the ovipositor, consisting of two parts of valves. There are many different shapes and sizes of ovipositor, but that of the Ensifera of the Orthoptera is typical. It protrudes from the tip of the abdomen as a kind of sword, and the name Ensifera does mean 'sword-bearing'. In some cases the ovipositor functions in a surprising way. The Ichneumon Fly, *Rhyssa persuasoria*, Hymenoptera, has an extremely slender and flexible ovipositor with which it can

▼ Orthoptera (*Tettigonia*) with ovipositor

79

pierce wood and lay the egg directly in the body of the hymenopteran *Urocerus gigas*, which it parasites.

When there is no real ovipositor, the last abdominal segments function as a substitute ovipositor and can be extended like the sections of a telescope.

Once lodged inside a plant or tree or laid underground, the eggs are usually left to themselves. But sometimes the attention of the mother is more complex. The Aculate, Hymenoptera, the insects more familiar as Bees, Wasps and Ants, display the highest degree of insect instinct and intellect in their building of nests and provision of food supplies for the larvae. Here are a few of the well known examples of their parental care. The Pompilidae or Spider-hunting Wasps provide their larvae with spiders. Unafraid of the spiders' poisonous hooks, they do not even spurn such alarming prey as Tarantula. The shelters where they store the spiders are built in a variety of places. The wasp family Sphecidae, distinguished often by their long narrow-waisted abdomen, have more varied prey. *Ammophila* captures caterpillars; *Cerceris* usually likes weevils and beetles of the Buprestidae family; *Sphex* prefers Grasshoppers and Mantids. The basic problem for all these hunters is immobilizing their prey. The larva needs fresh food, but a large grasshopper or spider is hardly going to allow some defenceless little larva to nibble away at it. And so at the moment of capture the wasp stings the prey and kills, or more often paralyses it. It can no longer do any harm, but it is now an enormous lifeless burden, and moving it to the ready-prepared nest is a difficult task. *Sphex*, for example, drags its grasshopper prey by the antennae, walking backwards and coping on the way with the endless obstacles presented by the uneven ground.

Some prey is easier to capture than others. While a caterpillar has no weapons which its predator need fear, the same cannot be said of a bee. Yet *Philanthus*, a particular enemy of Bees, is unconcerned by their sting and is able to catch them without too much risk. Many species provide the larvae with small-sized prey, and have to supply a number of them to satisfy their offspring's needs. Others succeed in immobilizing colossal prey, like *Scolia* which attacks the large larvae of the Rhinoceros Beetle. These live underground and so *Scolia* has to carry out a subterranean search to find them.

Species of Hymenoptera which feed their offspring on honey and pollen do not have to struggle with a victim desperate to survive. Instead, the flowers they frequent seem to do all they can to attract these pollen-bearers.

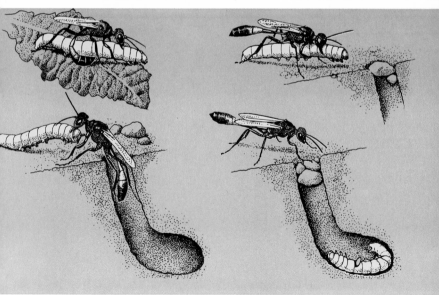

▲ Ammophila Wasp with caterpillar prey carried to the nest

81

## Sexual Dimorphism

In insects, differences between individuals of the two sexes
cover a whole range, from species in which male and female are
almost exactly identical, except for the genital organs, to others
where the two are so totally different that it is hard to believe
they belong to the same species.

Generally speaking the male is smaller than the female, but
more mobile and showy. Sometimes, the only difference is
colour, as with many species of Moths and Butterflies, and this
is called dichronism.

female

male

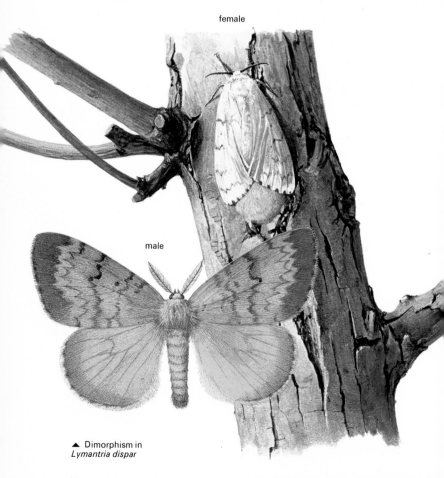

▲ Dimorphism in
*Lymantria dispar*

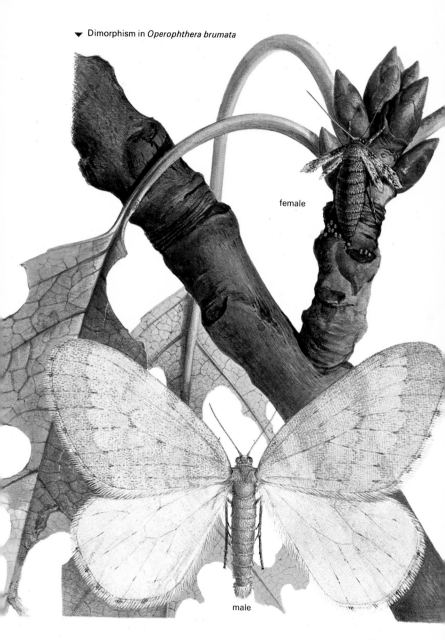

▼ Dimorphism in *Operophthera brumata*

female

male

83

▼ Female (left) and male (right) of Stag-beetles

## Alternation of Generations

Walking through fields in high summer you will soon notice
grass plant stems enclosed in a dark coloured or green sheath.
A closer inspection will show a quantity of tiny insects, so close
to one another that they seem to form an unbroken surface.
Anyone who grows roses will be only too familiar with the
harmful effects of insects similar to these. In both cases the
insects are Aphids or Greenfly, small insects of Homoptera
which are of interest here because of their reproductive
peculiarities.

▼ Apple Psyllid

To understand these peculiarities, we must distinguish
between two functions of reproduction: one is the straight
forward propagation of the species, the other, the less obvious
but equally important exchange of the genetic material which
governs the organism's development and functions. In normal
sexual reproduction, whether performed by separate sexes or

hermaphroditically, the two functions are generally combined in a pair of individuals. In Aphids, however, they are performed by different individuals in successive generations. In other words in each species of Aphid some individuals are destined to increase the numbers of the species, others to exchange genetic material.

In addition to this remarkable feature, some Aphids choose to live on different plants at different times of the year, a phenomenon known as host alternation. Although this must help to promote the survival of the species, it brings new

▼ Single cycle of
*Aphis pomi*

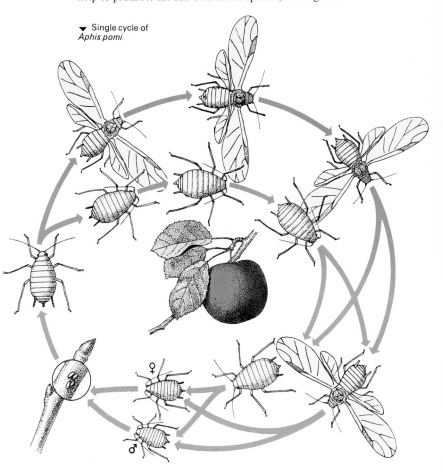

87

problems. Let us take as an example the life cycle of aphids which live on a single plant species, assuming that each species will be adapted to its own particular cycle. In the spring a wingless female develops from an egg laid during the previous autumn. Without mating with a male she produces many more females by a process of parthenogenesis or virgin birth. These in turn give birth parthenogenetically, producing a series of generations which include some winged individuals with the function of diffusing the species. At the end of the summer both males and females appear and reproduce in the normal way.

▼ Two-host cycle of *Hyalopterus pruni*

The fertilized female produces the eggs which will survive the winter and give birth to the female founders of new colonies.

Sometimes the cycle is confined to a single plant species, but often two types of plants are involved. In this case, the succession of parthenogenetic females includes a winged generation which migrates from one plant species to another, on which the rest of the cycle will take place. The cycle is completed by a migration back to the first host and by the appearance of males and non-parthenogenetic females.

The Woolly Apple Aphid reveals a feature characteristic of many Aphids: it produces wax which is exuded in the form of tiny balls, either from two little horns on the tip of the abdomen or from special glands in various parts of the body. An attack of Aphids on plants and trees often produces particular types of tumours or galls.

The cycles involving a secondary host affect many pairs of plants. With *Hyalopterus pruni* the two are a fruit tree, such as Peach or Plum, and Marsh Reed; *Forda trivialis* passes from the Turpentine-tree to the roots of grasses; in *Erisoma lanuginosum* the hosts are Pear and Elm. Clearly moving between such different plants involves both physiological and structural changes. The phenomenon is not random, but is governed by genetic and environmental factors, such as hours of daylight and the temperature. Finally, Aphids do not attack the same parts of different plants. Often, on one plant the green parts are attacked, while on the other it is the roots.

▼ *Phylloxera*: Below: Galls on a leaf. Right: a fundatrix, the wingless form and the winged sexual form.

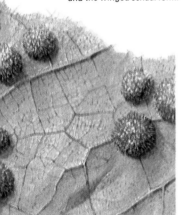

# Habits

Earlier pages have described the tools with which insects carry on their struggle for existence, and the way these vary as the insect develops. We shall now see how insects use these tools, always exploiting them to the full.

Like all animals, insects encounter a whole range of problems, but they fall under two main headings: the search for food and defence against enemies. The first type takes many forms, depending on the animal's diet. The food supply may be stable, like a tree-trunk or dead leaves lying on the ground: in this case the insect will not have many problems of movement, unless it has to leave its environment for some exceptional reason. On the

other hand, insects which do not have stable food supplies have to be very mobile to find their food, wherever it may be. Insects often have exceptional power of colonization: plant pests which have reached Europe from America have spread through the continent with alarming speed and become real scourges.

Defence against natural enemies is an equally serious problem. Often it can only be overcome by being extreme prolific, since individual insects are practically defenceless and each generation has to allow for a large number of losses in order to survive. Each species has ways of defending itself against food shortage and unfavourable environments; it can, for example, migrate or enter a resting stage of life. Escaping an enemy is often more difficult. The insect can flee, camouflage itself, use poisons in its blood, terrify its assailant or spray it with toxic substances; yet what can it do against the stealthiest of parasites, selected over millions of generations, which is about to inject its offspring into the victim's body with its ovipositor? What can a wood-eating larva do when the parasite's ovipositor seeks it out even inside the tree-trunk?

In the insect world, like our own, there are non-specialists and specialists. The non-specialists are not too particular about climate, not too choosy about their food and so can be found almost everywhere. Species which feed on different foods, even food of the same type, are described as polyphagous. The unspecialized insect is found in different environments and can tolerate considerable changes in its environment; frequently it is not even defeated by man's attempts to destroy it.

The specialist is more demanding. It eats only one type of food, or else it cannot tolerate marked changes in its conditions; if it is aquatic it can only tolerate a particular level of oxygenation in the water; if it is a parasite it only attacks one particular type of victim. In any given environment, specialists and non-specialists exist side by side in competition. In optimum conditions the specialist has the edge over the non-specialist, since its tools are better adapted, but faced with environmental change which alters the conditions which suit it best, the specialist succumbs, unable to adapt quickly to change.

In any environment, land or water, there are some organisms which produce organic material and others which consume it. Production is mainly the task of green plants and is effected by means of chlorophyll and the process of photosynthesis; consumption falls to animals and plants without chlorophyll. Insects are bracketed with the consumers, but at various levels. Some attack plants directly, some feed on animals, some are content with decaying material of animal or vegetable origin. Plant-eating insects are described as phytophagous and can be further subdivided: some attack only the parts of plants above ground, some only those below ground, some eat the wood, others the leaves. But that is not all. A food substance which to us appears homogeneous is not so at all to an insect. A tree trunk for example may house species which only eat the part just under the bark and others which go further on, right to the centre. The insect can distinguish and appreciate differences which to us seem negligible; what to us is a minimal difference in composition, to the insect is considerable and determines whether or not it can make use of it as food. Similarly, insects are affected by minimal environmental differences. What we think of as climate is very different from the climate which surrounds a small animal. In a field the air above the grass will be one temperature, among the grass another and near the soil yet another. Two neighbouring fields covered with different types of vegetation will reveal different climatic conditions. We should think in terms not of climate, but of micro-climate, the conditions found in a specific and limited part of an environment. It is surprising how many different insects there are in a field, in the ground or on the bank of a river. Most individuals belong to a limited number of species and many species contain only a few individuals. This rich variety of fauna is explained by the range of micro-environments present in any given environment, each of which may have a specialized inhabitant, perhaps linked to a particular plant, which can only live in certain parts of the area under consideration, or perhaps a parasite only of a particular species of insect. Not all environments contain the same number of species. The number depends on climatic conditions, and the amount and variety of food available. Dry environments, for example, obviously contain few species, but a field of corn will not contain so very many species either, even if there is an enormous number of individual insects.

The dispersion of a species is made easier if the species is able to move from place to place effectively, and the presence of wings in adult insects is, of course, very important. But this phenomenon often follows precise laws and is in no way fortuitous. A factor which limits the dispersion of many species, even those which can fly very well, is their tendency to occupy an exact territory. The spring song of many male birds is recognized to be a sign of the supremacy which the bird intends to establish over a given territory and a warning to possible intruders to keep away. Many insects behave in a similar way. Butterfly collectors know that the beautiful Red Admiral, which is so difficult to catch because of the way it springs into powerful flight, tends always to fly in the same place and even to rest on the same spot. A patient wait often rewards the hunter with his desired prey. Many Dragonflies behave similarly, and if driven away return obstinately to their point of departure. No doubt there are also many other less obvious examples.

The way insects form groups is also governed by a set rule which can at times be baffling. Many species show a so-called group effect which means the individuals which have developed in isolation differ from those which have grown in groups, not only in behaviour but also in certain characteristics of form and colour.

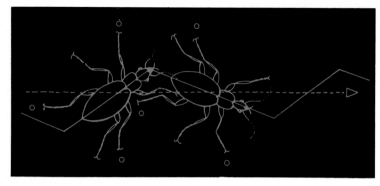

▲ Diagram of Carabid walking

## How Insects Walk

We know that with very few exceptions all insects have six legs, so that the problem of locomotion is basically the same for all of them. Firstly, the movement of the different limbs has to be coordinated, so that there is a constant and stable support as

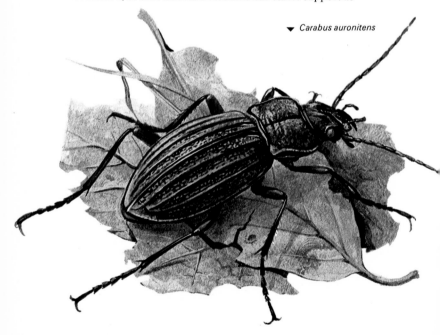

▼ *Carabus auronitens*

the insect advances. As an insect walks it always rests on three legs – the fore and hind leg on one side, the middle leg on the other: it has thus balanced on a kind of tripod so that the other legs can be lifted and moved forward. The same procedure follows with the other legs. Walking in this way, the insect does not follow a perfectly straight line, and if watched closely can be seen to proceed in a slightly winding fashion.

Insects are not equally agile, and indeed many are slow and ungainly. Runners can easily be identified by their long, slender legs without highly developed adhesive pads on the tarsus. Ground beetles of the family Carabidae are typical in shape. Mainly nocturnal insects, without functional wings under the elytra, they are slender in form and swift in movement. Beetles of the family Tenebrionidae which live in dry places, often even in deserts, have legs which are equally cursorial (adapted for running). Many Ants can also be counted as runners, but unlike these Beetles they can also move quickly on plants.

Insects can climb more or less anywhere and the ability to move on vertical surfaces is indispensable for many species, especially for plant-feeders. For this reason, the end of the leg

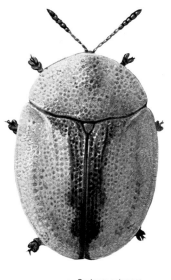

▲ Sedentary insect
(*Cassida*)

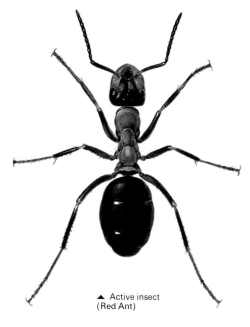

▲ Active insect
(Red Ant)

95

bears a pair of curved claws. In some species, such as certain
Beetles of the family Scarabaeidae, these claws have a special
function: they can fold right back on the tarsus and so act as
little pincers. This means the insect can attach itself to slender
stems and so move agily among the intricate inflorescences of
many plants, for example Umbelliferae.

The claws are not much use for clinging to smooth surfaces,
and are often helped by an adhesive pad on the bottom of the
tarsus, which may consist of pulvilli and the so-called arolium,
an organ typical of Diptera, for example, House-flies.

If walking on the ground is quite a problem and on plants
even more so, then walking on water seems quite impossible.
Not so for insects, however, which manage without too much
difficulty. On the surface of stagnant or slow-flowing water one
can often see long-bodied insects with extremely slender legs
darting swiftly across the water, often in groups. They look like
Spiders but are in fact insects, members of Heteroptera to be
precise. Known as Pond-skaters (*Gerris*), these insects walk on
the water by exploiting two factors: firstly the surface tension
of the water, creating a film which will support very small
objects, and secondly the length of the insect's limbs which
with the tarsi provide adequate support. Other heteropteran
insects which copy the Pond-skater in walking on the water
include the slow-moving *Hydrometra* or Water Gnat with its
hesitant forward movement, and the family Vellidae, typified
by the Water Cricket which is similar to the Pond-skater but
stouter and with shorter legs. Besides the insects which walk on
the water by exploiting the surface tension, there are also some
which walk in it. Some Water or Hydrophilid Beetles, in fact,
move beneath the surface film of the water, stomach upwards.
Some Staphylinid or Rove Beetles of the *Stenus* species have a
curious way of moving on water. These insects, which have a
short elyctra, bulging eyes and special mouth parts resembling
those of Dragonfly larvae, almost always live on the banks of
water-courses, ponds and marshes. Besides moving normally
on the water, they must, like all insects which live near water,
be able to manage in special circumstances like floods, or when
having to flee across small stretches of water quickly. On the tip
of the abdomen they have special glands which secrete a liquid
which has the property of lowering the surface tension. If they
touch the film of the water with the abdomen and let out a little
liquid they receive a thrust which moves them suddenly
forward. Many hymenopteran predators like Sphecid or
Pompilid Wasps hunt their prey on the wing, but drag it back
to the nest on foot.

## Leaping

One of the insect's most effective ways of escaping an enemy is by causing bewilderment. Quick flight is not enough; the insect must disappear unexpectedly, without showing where it has gone. This, briefly, is the function of leaping in insects, a feature in many of them and achieved in a great variety of ways. In insects the leap is the initial act of flight and not an intrinsic part of it, as in vertebrates. It is far more developed than in almost any other animal: the jump of a Flea or Grasshopper makes the insect cover a prodigious distance.

▼ Grasshoppers of the genus *Oedipoda*

Collembola:
▼ Springtail (Arthropleona)

▲ Springtail (Symphypleona)

99

▲ Fulgoroid leafhopper with egg masses

Leaping insects belong to many different groups. Almost all members of Collembola, Aphaniptera and Orthoptera leap, as do some species of Hemiptera, a few of Coleoptera, Mecoptera and Diptera and a small number of others. Usually insects jump with their legs, but Collembola, or Spring-tails, are a notable exception. They have two special appendages: the furcula which is the actual springing organ, and the retinaculum which is complementary to it. The furcula is a forked appendage attached to the fourth abdominal segment which is folded under the abdomen and held in place by the retinaculum, a short double appendage ending in two claws. When the Springtail needs to flee it suddenly releases the furcula which hits the ground and makes the insect take a leap backwards. All Collembola do not jump equally well: some move only a little, but others disappear from sight quite suddenly.

The prime examples of jumping insects are Orthoptera, better known as Grasshoppers, Crickets and Locusts. The jumping organ is formed by the hind legs, and in particular by the enlarged and very muscular femur and the slender but very rigid tibia which is often equipped with spines. The joint between femur and tibia is the source of the insect's spring. Many Grasshoppers when disturbed combine leaping and flight, unfolding the hind wings which are kept folded like a fan when at rest. Some species like the European *Oedipoda* have brightly coloured hind wings, while their general colouring is

100

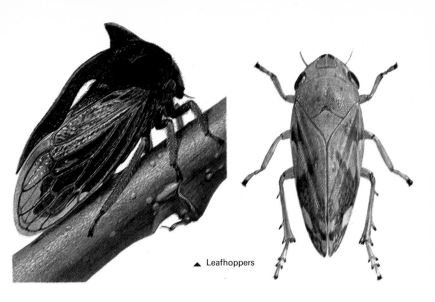

▲ Leafhoppers

mimetic and merges well with stony settings. The fleeing insect suddenly turns into a splash of flying colour.

The Leaf hopper (Homoptera) leap is always achieved by means of the hind legs, but as the muscles involved are inside the thorax the legs are not particularly developed.

▼ Rhododendron Leafhopper (*Graphocephala*)

101

## Sessile Insects

There are many sea creatures which at least for part of their life are unable to move from place to place; sponges and corals are two examples. On dry land the situation must surely be different, since the very term 'land animal' suggests a mobile organism which can walk, crawl or fly. But this is not always the case. Showing yet again how highly adaptable insects are, there are many species which for a period of their life do not move at all and are transformed to such an extent that they even lose the basic attributes of insects. This occurs particularly in the homopteran family Coccidae, also known as Scale Insects or Mealy Bugs.

Everyone must have noticed little brown oval scales on oranges; they come off easily, but it is not possible to tell what they really are from their form and structure. In fact, these little incrustations are insects – female Coccids which are transformed in shape and protected by a covering known as a follicle. Male Coccids look like ordinary insects, with wings and legs, but they too have some unusual features: their mouth apparatus, for instance, is rudimentary and non-functional and they have two wings instead of four. Another characteristic of Coccids, besides the females' weird structure, is the way they produce secretions such as lac and wax. Wax and lac have similar protective functions, but may also be used in the formation of the egg sac.

For centuries man has exploited the coccids' special

▼ Male of Coccid (*Icerya purchasi*)

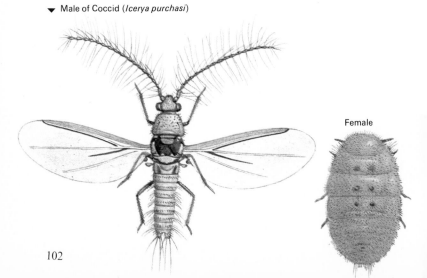

Female

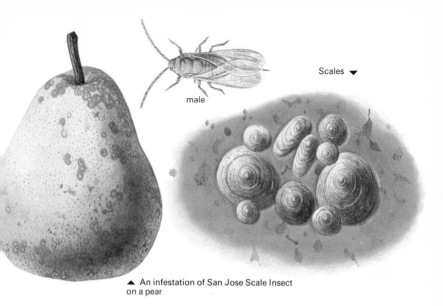

Scales ▼

male

▲ An infestation of San Jose Scale Insect on a pear

secretions in a number of ways. Not many people realize that Coccids help to make shellac, vermilion and alkermes. Lac is a special secretion of some exotic Coccids which becomes extremely hard on contact with the air, and is used in preparation of shellac and other varnishes. Vermilion, for dyeing fabrics, used to be derived from an Oak Scale Insect, and the colour of alkermes also comes from a Scale Insect. There is also cochineal which is derived from the Cochineal Insect *Dactyloplus coccus*.

▼ Mussel Scale on Mandarins

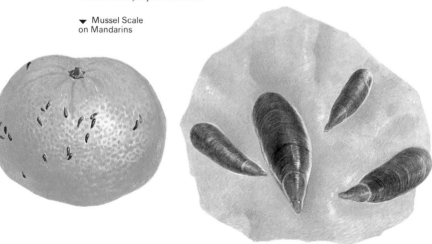

## Flight

A group of Hover Flies poised, apparently motionless, between light and shade in a wood during the summer seems an unexceptional sight. Yet this ability to stay in the air, a supreme achievement of the animal world, reaches its highest level in insects which gradually acquired this characteristic in the course of evolution. Probably, to start with, expansions of the thorax appeared which made gliding flight possible. Movement of these expansions followed as certain muscles developed. With the right muscles flight became possible, and different groups of insects, each in its own way, took to the air. The group of winged insects considered to be the most primitive, Ephemeroptera or Mayflies, are also very poor fliers; their wing beat is rather slow, their flight heavy and they have little active steering ability. Dragonflies, with a close network of cross veins on their wings, get on much better, although they still have some marked primitive characteristic. Zyoptera or Damsel Flies are rather slow, but Anisoptera or true Dragonflies are among the better fliers. Their flight is often powerful and they can remain stationary, but they can also take off suddenly in case of danger or when there is a prey to catch.

Orthoptera are not usually great fliers. Most Grasshoppers take a leap, then a short flight and settle a little further on. In the Migratory Locusts of the same order, however, the wing becomes a powerful instrument, making possible the dreaded migrations of these voracious swarms. Hemiptera, both Heteroptera and Homoptera, are not great fliers; for example, if a Stink Bug comes indoors it will keep bumping into walls and will be quite unable to avoid obstacles, though some hemipterans do better than this. The flight of Neuroptera and Trichoptera is slow on the whole. Among Lepidoptera, there is a great range of ability. Butterflies, the day-flying species also known as Rhopalocera, have a slow wing beat, but because of the large size of their wings they are usually capable of gliding flight; this feature is well developed in members of the family Nymphalidae. Moths usually fly with a remarkably rapid wing beat; this is true of the family Sphingidae or Hawk Moths, and particularly of *Macroglossa* which can stay motionless for some time in front of flowers, exploring for food with their long probiscis. Coleoptera usually fly badly; clumsy and heavy, they are scarcely able to steer at all and can only take off after lengthy preparations. In the air they usually keep the elytra open to provide a plane. The Cetonid Beetles are an exception, as their elytra cannot spread, and so remain closed in flight.

Insect in flight ▶

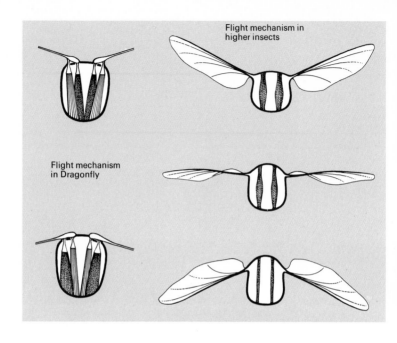

Flight mechanism in higher insects

Flight mechanism in Dragonfly

Hymenoptera are usually good fliers; they move through the air in a gentle rather dancing manner, especially Bees and the large-bodied Bumble Bees. Worker Ants are wingless, as are the queens after their nuptial flight, but there are also winged male and female Ants which are very poor fliers: when swarming they often meet with a mass death, falling to the ground in large numbers. The best fliers are to be found in Diptera. Although there are some poor fliers, like the Tipulidae or Crane-flies, many Flies cannot be surpassed for endurance and accurate steering. Besides the Hoverflies, already mentioned, there are the little flies, found especially in houses in the country; they can fly for hours, hovering motionless in the air, their wings beating swiftly, then darting off unexpectedly. As well as different styles of flying, there are various rest positions for the wings. There are three basic attitudes: wings closed vertically over the body, wings open horizontally, and wings forming a roof over the body. The first position which is the rarest and most primitive occurs in Ephemeroptera or Mayflies, the most ancient winged insects, and also, slightly modified, in Damsel Flies. It also appears in

▲ Bee-fly (Bombilidae)

Moths, in which it has a mimetic function as will be shown later. The second position is found in Dragonflies which can often be seen resting on stems near water, their large wings open and motionless. The roof-like cover over the body is the commonest position found, for example, in Orthoptera, Hemiptera (Heteroptera and Homoptera), Coleoptera, Diptera and Hymenoptera. As a modification of this position, many groups fold their hindwings like a fan, so that the wings take up a minimum of space for their size. Skippers; butterflies of the family Hesperidae, have a curious resting position, with the forewings held vertically and the hindwings kept open horizontally: however, if frightened they assume the usually vertical butterfly position.

Wing movement is produced by a powerful system of muscles. Insect muscles are far more numerous than those of vertibrates, and given the small size of insects, their performance is not really surprising.

## Strong Fliers

The insect collector, so often humorously portrayed, butterfly net in hand, as a comic figure in a world of his own, in fact acquires great familiarity with insect habits, particularly those of flying insects. It is not easy to capture powerful fliers like Butterflies or Dragonflies and the present writer, a butterfly hunter in his spare time, knows what is involved in the long waits, the sudden darting flight and the sad disappointment of failure. Large Dragonflies, especially *Anax*, are particularly troublesome. One arrives suddenly over the water where it hovers motionless; the collector is about to reach out with his net, when it moves away; it returns and the hunter strikes – but misjudges the distance. This can go on for hours as the insect is so attached to its territory that it constantly returns as if

▼ *Anax imperator*

mockingly, although it is really just responding to an instinctive stimulus which draws it to that stretch of land and water. The same happens with some butterflies. The families Nymphalidae and Apaturidae are typical specimens of our climate and catching the superb *Charaxes* or the large *Limenitis populi* and *Apatura iris* (Purple Emperor), is an unforgettable experience. *Charaxes* is a very swift flier found in Mediterranean scrubland; it loves the sun and the *Arbutus*, which acts as host to its handsome green caterpillar. The second two, similar in shape and habits, like shady woods. Looking up through the branches, one can often see their silhouettes, high up against the light. They float lightly, and it seems that if they would only come lower the hunter's task would be easy. The more experienced hunters know where to

▲ *Charaxes jasius*

look for them, near damp patches on the bare ground left by puddles. There the situation changes. The peaceful flier from the heights settles on the ground, spreads its large black wings with their white spots and licks the ground in search of water. Now is the moment to strike – but there is no margin of error. If the insects notice the trap or the first attempt fails, it darts swiftly away; the first zig-zag movements bewilder the hunter and then with a sudden flurry the butterfly returns to its heights.

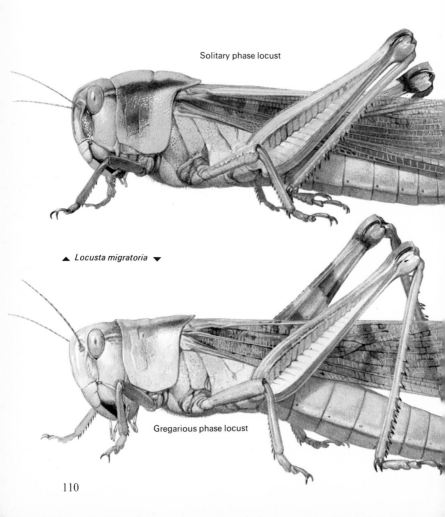

Solitary phase locust

▲ *Locusta migratoria* ▼

Gregarious phase locust

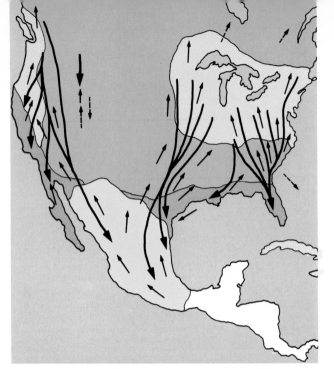

Group of Monarch Butterflies

◀ Migration routes of Monarch Butterfly      ▲ Monarch Butterfly

### Migrations

Locusts were one of the seven plagues of Egypt and when dense swarms of these insects migrate the effects are horrifying: wherever they stop nothing is left of any plant, which they attack with their powerful jaws. The phenomenon occurs in several different species of Orthoptera, of the sub-order Caelifera, and although it has been known to occur on a small scale in Europe, only occasional stragglers reach the British Isles. The most extraordinary thing is that the species which move in these ravening hordes are simply the offspring of peaceful solitary grasshoppers, yet the two forms of the same species, solitary and gregarious, are different not only in habits but also in colour and shape. The appearance of the gregarious phase (the successive forms are described as phases) is produced by a group effect.

Many Butterflies also move in large numbers, although their migrations are not a threat to agriculture. The Painted Lady (*Cynthia cardui*), a Nymphalid butterfly which has tawny wings with black and white spots, is found almost everywhere. In spring it leaves the warm regions and moves north, getting as far as Iceland.

**Predators**

Long, sharp mandibles, slender legs for running, agility and aggressiveness are common characteristics of many predatory insects, more particularly of those which actively seek out their prey. The Carabidae, or Ground Beetles, and many Ants are the best known examples. These Beetles, sometimes sombre in appearance but often brightly metallic in colour, are typically nocturnal animals. Hiding under stones, they wait for night to seek their prey. Some are not too choosy about their food and in lean periods will even make do with a vegetarian diet, but others are specialized in form and in their search of prey. They include members of the genus *Cychrus*, which have an elongated head and thorax in order to reach snails inside their shells. Ground Beetles' food supply depends on solitary attack, but with Ants the gregarious instinct makes it possible for them to overcome prey of colossal size. Caterpillars are among their

▼ Wood Ants (*Formica rufa*) swarming over a caterpillar

favourite victims, so much so that in some places the Wood Ant (*Formica rufa*) is protected by law because of its capacity for destroying these hungry pests; it is even taken to areas where it is not usually found in order to counteract the destructive action of these dreadful forest parasites. Not only do predatory insects go out looking for their victims; some are masters of ambush. The Praying Mantis is almost invisible in the green grass, as, forelegs folded against its thorax, it waits for some unfortunate passing insect which will be unable to escape the sudden thrust of those hooked limbs. The grim reputation of this insect rests on the female's habit of eating the male during mating. This horrifying fact is explained by the female's need for a rich supply of protein at the moment when she has to lay her eggs and make an ootheca for them. The Cicindelidae or Tiger Beetles are, as adults, very active and mobile predators, one of the few species of beetle which can take off in flight suddenly, without any preparations. The larva, however, lives in holes which it digs for itself in the

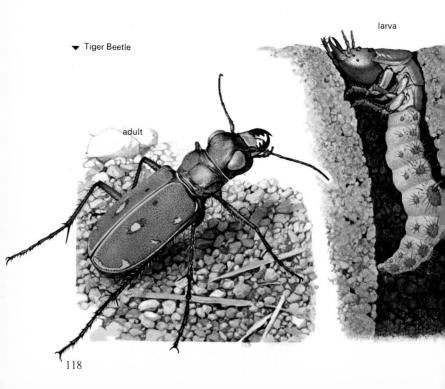

Tiger Beetle

larva

adult

Ant-lion

adult

larva

Capture of an Ant

119

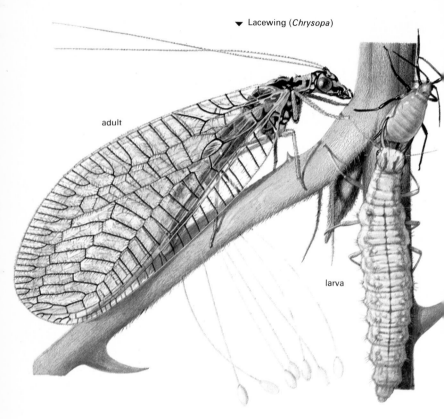

▼ Lacewing (*Chrysopa*)

adult

larva

ground and there it lies in wait, its head level with the soil. This method of ambush has led to a curious modification of the insect's mouth parts; instead of facing forwards or downwards as in the vast majority of insects, they point upwards ready to snatch any unfortunate prey which passes by. The Tiger Beetle larva's method of ambush appears again in the Ant-lion which, again in the larval stage, is a skilful builder of traps. This insect digs itself little holes, in a shape of an inverted cone, in sandy grounds and waits at the bottom, covered in sand. If an insect falls into the hole a landslide of sand will engulf it. The Ant-lion will throw sand over it, burying it further. As soon as it is within the predator's reach the victim is done for. It is grasped by poisonous pincer-like mandibles which have a little channel along which the haemolymph is sucked. The adult Ant-lion in

▲ Nymph and adult of the Assassin Bug

no way resembles the stumpy form of the predatory larva; it is an elegant winged-insect, not unlike a Dragonfly. A relation of the Ant-lion, *Chrysopa* (Lacewings) has, as a larva, a very similar mouth apparatus, but instead of lying in ambush it turns its attention to one of the easiest and most abundant forms of prey for a predator, Aphids. The Aphid colonies have no defence against the predator's sharp mandibles and so are slaughtered without any of the victims' usual convulsive attempts to save themselves. Another distinctive feature of these insects is their habit of laying their eggs at the end of a long thread produced by the mother. Obviously, such an attractive food supply as Aphids is not attacked only by *Chrysopa*. Many other insects favour these little barrel-shaped creatures.

## Parasites

Various species of parasitic insects have been mentioned in earlier pages. Parasitism is not the simple, easy way of life it may sound. Initially, at least, the parasite does not seek to bring about its victim's death, and its own life is in fact dependent on its host's. It may even have enemies of its own to contend with.

Like other animals, some insects display relationships which seem parasitic, but cannot strictly speaking be defined as such. For example, the *Braula coeca* or Bee-louse, a small member of Diptera, without eyes or wings, lives on Hive-bees but feeds simply on honey from the host's mouth. The true parasite is much less moderate in its demands. Its attack may simply cause its victim annoyance, but it is often more harmful, or even fatal. It may attack the body of its victim inside (in which case it is known as an endoparasite) or from outside (ectoparasite).

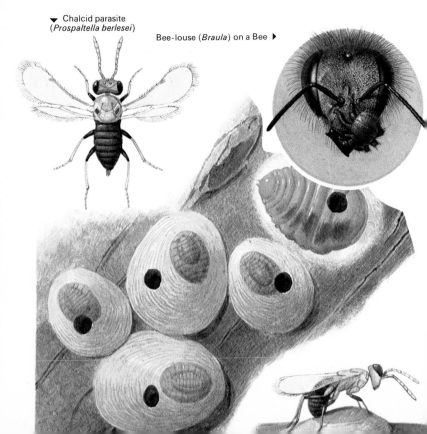

▼ Chalcid parasite
(*Prospaltella berlesei*)

Bee-louse (*Braula*) on a Bee ▶

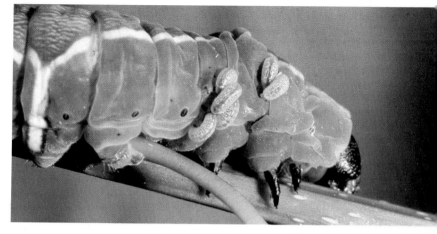

▲ Parasitised caterpillar

Endoparasites include many members of the two orders
Hymenoptera and Diptera. The Hymenoptera, in particular
Chalcids, Braconids and Ichneumons, mainly attack other
insects and their favourite victims are larvae with soft
integuments. The female parasite uses her ovipositor to lay her
eggs on or within the larva. In the early stages the parasites do

▼ Parasitised caterpillar

not feed on the vital organs and this allows the host to survive for the time being.

Another favourite source of food for parasites is provided by the oothecae or egg purses of many insects. The Cockroach's, for example, shelters the curious *Evania appendigaster* with its strangely shaped abdomen; the segments are separated by a stalk or petiole and the first segment is flattened vertically. Minute insects, like Aphids and Coccidae, as well as large ones, may be attacked by parasites. Often, the parasite itself is parasitized, in which case the attacking organism is known as a hyperparasite. Parasitic insects are of vital importance to our environment in establishing biological equilibrium, since the prolific way in which insects multiply is harmless only if large numbers of individual insects are destroyed. Parasites play a greater part than predators in keeping down numbers.

So far we have dealt with Hymenoptera, but Diptera include many parasites too. They also include many blood-sucking species which attack vertebrates. These include Mosquitoes, Horseflies and Tsetse Flies, all of which feed on blood.

However, Diptera, which as larvae are internal parasites of mammals, are less well known. The *Oestrus ovis* or Sheep-nostril Fly which attacks sheep is one example. The larva lives in a strange part of the victim's body. The eggs are laid near the animal's nostrils and the larvae then crawl through the nostrils to the nasal cavities and sinuses behind the frontal bone which connect with the nasal fossae. This causes the sheep much discomfort and may even lead to death. The

▼ *Hippobosca equina*　　　　　　　　　　▼ *Oestrus ovis*

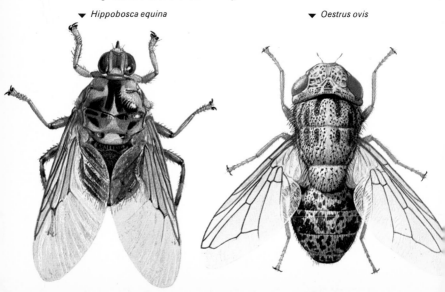

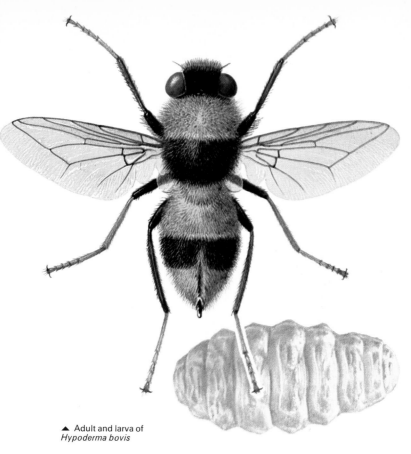

▲ Adult and larva of
*Hypoderma bovis*

Warble-fly, *Hypoderma bovis*, follows a different route. After a long journey inside the cow's digestive system it reaches the subcutaneous tissue. Here, when it reaches maturity, it makes a hole through the skin to reach the ground where it pupates. Obviously, such habits, besides causing the animal discomfort, do harm financially by damaging the hides. The harmful effect of Bot-flies (*Gasterophilus*) is even more direct. They lay their eggs on the hide of horses so that when the animals lick themselves they are inadvertently contaminated by the newly-hatched larvae. The larvae reach the mucous lining of the digestive system and do much damage. Another species of Diptera, which attacks horses, is the so-called Horsefly, a flattened fly which, rather than completing a stage of its life-cycle inside the mammal, simply irritates it from outside as an ectoparasite.

Man is no more immune than other vertebrates to insect attack. The current gradual disappearance of many parasites which used to cause irritation and constitute a serious health hazard is due entirely to greater care over hygiene. Three human ectoparasites are unfortunately well known: Lice, Fleas and Bedbugs. They belong to quite different groups, but have certain characteristics in common: secondary winglessness and a mouth apparatus of the piercing type. Lice are members of Anoplura, flattened insects which have legs with curved claws to grip the hair of the host animal. The Human Louse exists as two races, with some structural differences depending on whether it is a head louse (*Pediculus humanus captis*) or a body louse (*P. h. corporis*).

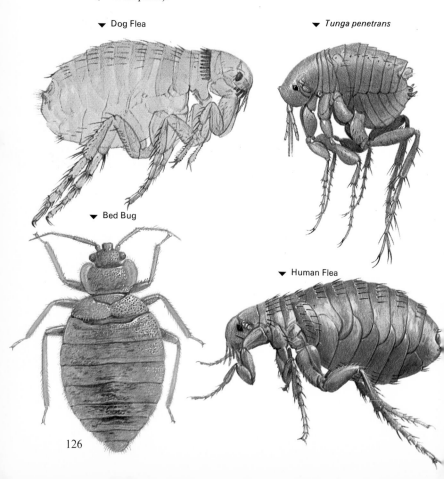

▼ Dog Flea

▼ *Tunga penetrans*

▼ Bed Bug

▼ Human Flea

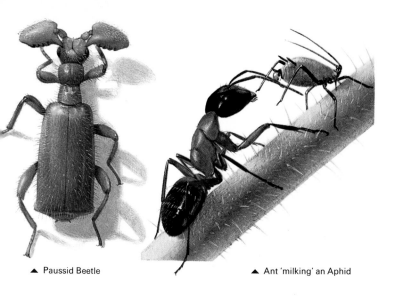

▲ Paussid Beetle

▲ Ant 'milking' an Aphid

**Commensals and parasites of ants**
Insect societies, with their amazingly complex and highly
developed relationships between individuals, might be expected
to be impenetrable to other animals. Indeed, for most of them
falling into an ants' nest means certain death. But some are
undeterred. Many insects, selected over the generations, brave
the danger and either operate as poachers inside the ants' nest
or establish a friendly relationship with the ants. There are
many examples, one of the best known being numerous
Aphids. These get protection from the Ants in return for drops
of sugary liquid exuded from the intestine. It has been
suggested that Ants may mistake the rear of an Aphid for the
head of one of their own kind and that they take the drop of
liquid because of the habit of exchanging food which exists
among social insects, a phenomenon known as trophallaxis.
Insects which habitually live in Ants' nests (and Ants even go
looking for Aphids outside the nest) are generally strange and
unusual in form, though this way may only affect parts of the
body (such as the antennae of the Paussidae). Practically
nothing is known about the purpose of such forms, although
they may be a mimetic phenomenon, but the function of the
many glands found all over these insects' bodies is more
obvious. Their secretions encourage friendly treatment on the
part of the Ants.

127

▼ Larvae of *Phalera bucephala*

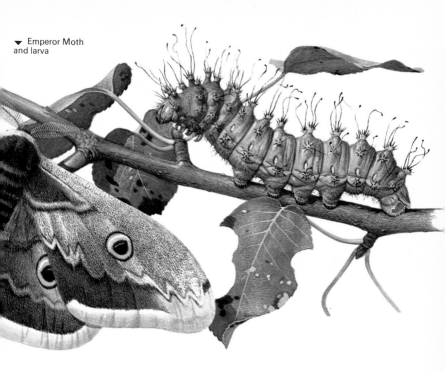

▼ Emperor Moth
and larva

### Leaf-eaters

An examination of the leaves of any plant will quickly show
that none is spared by devouring insects which nibble at the
edges and gnaw away the tissue to the thickest veins. Often,
practically nothing is left of the leaf. There are several
explanations for insects liking leaves. They are more tender and
digestible than wood, which can only be assimilated if there are
special micro-organisms in the intestine. They are more
abundant than seeds, a prime material, rich in nutritive
substances, but produced only sparingly by the plant.

Therefore, there is a host of leaf-eating or in scientific terms,
phytophagous insects. Many of them are moth and butterfly
caterpillars, with their brightly-coloured integuments or hairs
round their head in tufts forming a kind of fur. Although
sometimes solitary, they more often gather in greedy hordes
which may be protected by rough nests of silk. Some
caterpillars reach enormous size, that of the Great Peacock
Moth as much as four inches (ten centimetres). Others are
much smaller, and among these pygmy species the so-called
leaf-miners must be mentioned. These are the larvae of tiny
moths which live by burrowing galleries inside leaves. Their

▼ Adult, larva and eggs
of Chrysomelid Beetle
on Poplar

attack is visible from the outside as a translucent winding trail. Leaf-miners are modified in form and flattened to fit inside the thickness of the leaf. The larvae of some other insects behave in a similar way to these caterpillars. Leaf-eating is less widespread among Coleoptera than caterpillars, but it is still widespread and economically damaging. If you come across a sickly-looking tree in May and shake the branches you may well be hit by the hail of large Beetles, some of which will fly off with a low buzzing sound. This is the well-known Cock-chafer or Maybug, which after living in the ground for three years as a larva is now briefly enjoying the sun. Among the most avid leaf-eating beetles are the roundish, brightly-coloured Chrysomelidae. Every Poplar tree shelters in its leaves the Poplar Beetle, red and black as adult and white speckled with black as larva. Tastes which are too pungent for us do not put insects off: the Colorado Beetle of the same family greedily attacks potato leaves which we find uneatable because of the solanine they contain. The Criocerinae are unusually slender in form for Chrysomelid beetles, and are very bright coloured. Their favourite food is often plants of the family Liliaceae. Some species of the genus *Crioceris* live on asparagus; the red

130

▼ *Lilioceris lilii*

▼ Carabid Beetle (*Zabrus*) and larva

*Lilioceris* and its larva, covered with its own excrement, is found on lilies. The Elm, like the Poplar, is infested by its own particular chrysomelid: the greenish-yellow Elm Leaf Beetle. Among the Chrysomelids there is little to choose for strangeness between the Hispinae which are covered with sharp spines, so that they look like little hedgehogs, and the Tortoise Beetles (*Cassida*) which are like little shields with the legs scarcely peeping out below; they often have magnificent iridescent hues which disappear on death.

The Carabid Beetles have already been described as typical predators, but some of them prefer plants, like the shiny black *Zabrus* whose larvae feed on wheat leaves. This means the insect is harmful, though rare in these parts. The leaf-rolling members of the family Curculionidae (weevils) must be

▲ *Byctiscus betulae* and rolled leaves protecting larva

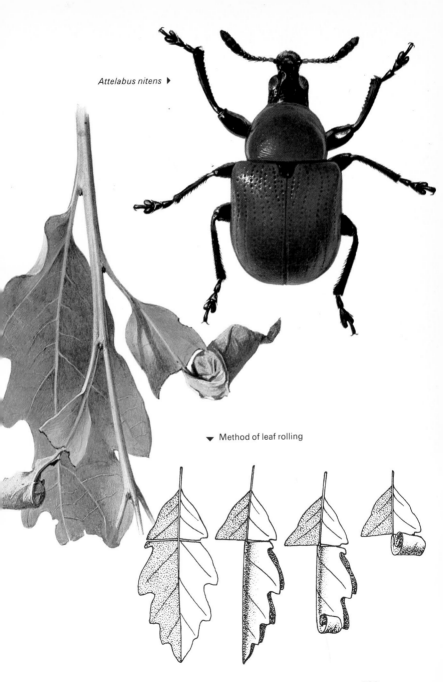

*Attelabus nitens* ▶

▼ Method of leaf rolling

133

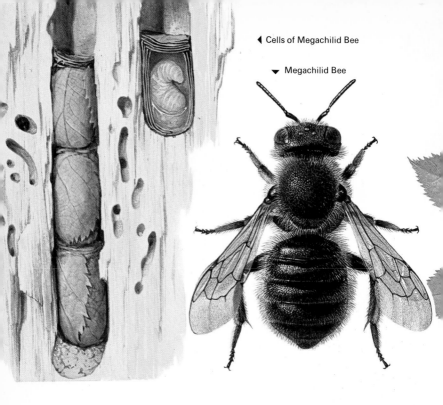

◀ Cells of Megachilid Bee

▼ Megachilid Bee

counted among the cleverest beetles in their use of leaves. They display remarkable skill in handling leaves which they use both as food supply and a shelter for the larvae. The work of *Byctiscus betulae* is one example: they roll up the leaves of trees to make an elongated roll like a cigar. To make the leaf wither and lose its stiffness the insect bites through the ribs of the leaf. The eggs are laid inside the 'cigar' and the larvae develop there. By the time the leaf is dry they are mature and so when the leaf drops they pupate in the ground.

*Attelabus nitens* behaves in a rather similar way to *Byctiscus*, with the further refinement that the whole leaf is not used to make the nest, but only the end part which is separated from the rest by an incision; the end is then rolled up from the tip and the insect makes a kind of barrel which remains hanging by the main rib. The long, patient work of these insects is, of course, exploited by other insects: certain species of parasites make their way into the ready-made cigar.

For Hymenoptera, the insects which display the highest level of instinct, leaves are not just a source of food, but may also

◀ Leaf incisions made by a Megachilid Bee

▲ Sawfly (*Caliroa limacina*)

provide a building material or a basis for cultivation. The most primitive forms of Hymenoptera, members of the sub-order Symphyta or sawflies, simply eat leaves, but the highly evolved Hymenoptera make different use of them. Bees of the family Megachilidae use them to make nests.

▼ Leaf Cutter Ants

## Wood Insects

Leaves have so many advantages as a food supply for insects that one might expect wood to be little favoured. This is far from being the case. Xylophagous insects, as the wood-eaters are called, are very numerous and are not hindered by the difficulties which the digestion and assimilation of cellulose may present.

Not all wood-boring insects are concerned with food. *Xylocopa violacea*, a large Carpenter Bee which has a velvety black body and dark wings with a bluish sheen, simply bores little cells for the larvae to grow in.

Xylophagous insects do not only attack living wood. Many prefer the wood of dying or dead trees, as is shown by the Wood Worm, which chews its way through our centuries-old furniture. It is important to remember that only the larvae feed on wood. The adults usually have different habits and often

▼ Carpenter bee *Xylocopa violacea*

Tunnels and pupae
cells of
*Xylocopa violacea* ▶

prefer flowers. These larvae are distinguished by certain common characteristics, even when they belong to different insect orders. They are cylindrical in shape with short legs or none, since they would in any case serve no purpose in wood galleries. They may, instead, have special surfaces suitable for clinging to the gallery walls to make movement easier. Usually they are whitish in colour (except for the red Goat Moth Caterpillar), the integument is very soft and the eyes are not well developed. On the other hand, the mouth parts are powerful for grinding up toughest fibres. Xylophagous insects belong to various orders. Although they include few Butterflies and Moths, since they, as we have seen, prefer tender leaves, one of the best known woodborers is a moth – the red caterpillar of the Goat Moth. The adult is an ugly moth with a dumpy body and greyish wings. The larva is a repellant dirty red tube with yellowish sides which bores galleries through

▼ Caterpillar and adult of Cossid Moth

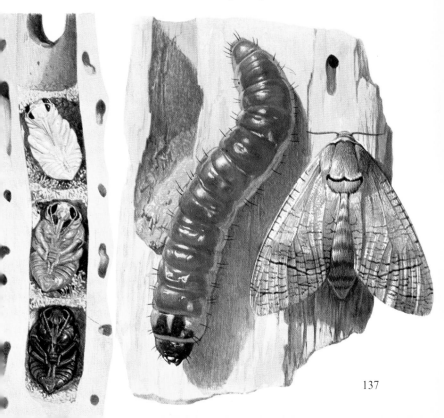

137

▲ Cerambycid Beetle

▼ Hyalotrupes

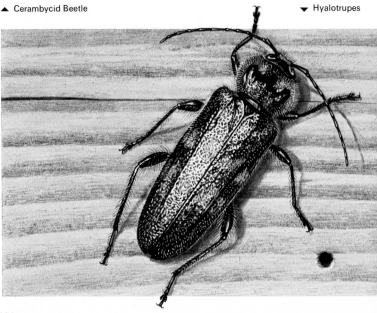

many trees such as apple, pear and poplar. Members of the moth family Sesiidae in the larval stage are also wood-feeders. The curious adults look so like wasps that only an experienced eye can see that they are moths, distantly related to the Red Admiral or the Cabbage White Butterfly.

The largest number of xylophagous insects are again to be found in Coleoptera, an enormous order displaying a whole range of habits. There are many species of xylophagous beetles which attack various tree species, each in its own way. The expert can examine the course of the galleries which the larvae make through wood, see whether they are on the surface or go deeper, and thus identify the species which caused them. The families Cerambycidae and Buprestidae include some of the most beautiful and also the strangest xylophagous insects. The Cerambycidae are also known as Long-horn Beetles because of the enormously developed antennae in some species. They vary in form and colour. Some are dark with glossy reliefs on their shell; others are striped and streaked to resemble wasps. Some of the adults are nocturnal, others are diurnal and feed on flowers. Among the best known is *Cerambyx cerdo*, one of the largest European beetles. Its larva completes a cycle lasting several years inside the wood of oak trees. When it is about to

*Lampra rutilans* (Bupestridae)

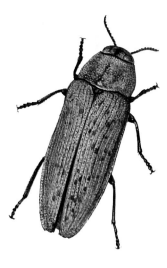

139

pupate the larva moves towards the surface of the trunk so that the adult, which is not able to bore through the wood very much, will not find it too difficult to get out. The Cerambycidae are highly valued by collectors, but the jewel-like Buprestidae are probably even more sought after. Their beauty lies not so much in their form, which is rather dumpy and inelegant, but in their superb, usually metallic colouring. Green, red and bronze combine to form simple but exceptionally fine patterns. In *Capnodis*, the black colouring with fine white designs produced by a waxy substance gives an impression of sober funeral garb. The larvae of Buprestidae are slightly different from those of Cerambycidae in that the thorax is rather broad and the abdomen correspondingly narrow. The head is fairly flattened. They also live on cultivated plants and may be harmful, as with *Capnodis tenebrionis* which lives on Peach and Plum trees.

If you carefully raise a piece of bark on a dying or dead tree you will find a large number of insects living in this micro-environment. Often these species feed both on wood and on the mycelia of fungus which have got under the bark and may be the reason for the tree's poor state of health. In many cases, these insects are surprisingly well adapted for living in the small space available under the bark. For example, if they have no capacity for boring their bodies are extremely flat.

The beetle family Cucujidae, which are almost all Bark-beetles, are similar in structure, as are some species of the families Ostomidae, Staphylinidae, Histeridae and some others. Some of these do not eat wood or fungi, but live as predators off other bark creatures. However, the insects found in the largest quantities underneath the bark are the Scolytidae, Beetles closed to the long-snouted Curculionidae or Weevils. They are not flat like the insects so far described; instead their body is perfectly cylindrical, since they really are wood-boring insects not just inquilines.

The effects of their activity are unmistakable. In the tree's bark or sapwood a regular network of fine galleries appears, looking rather like the characters of some mysterious cuneiform script. A look at the insects' habits explains this regular pattern. The galleries usually consist of a wider main gallery with more or less regular side galleries branching off, narrow at the start, widening at the end. There are many variations on this general scheme. The main gallery is the work of a fertilized adult female and is called the brood gallery. As she advances the female lays the eggs on the sides of the passage.

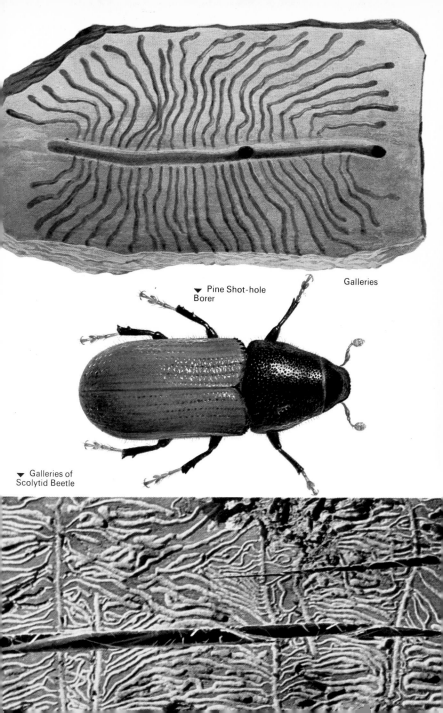

Galleries

▼ Pine Shot-hole Borer

▼ Galleries of Scolytid Beetle

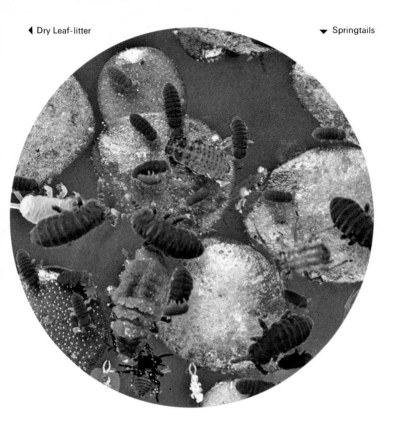

### Scavengers

The recycling of waste is one of the most serious problems which faces our industrialized society and one which has too long been neglected. However, in the balance of nature the problem is solved successfully and the combined action of scavenging animals is one of the key factors in the way ecosystems operate.

Many insects eat dead organic matter. A remarkable number of Beetles, for example, feed on plant remains. Obviously one little beetle cannot destroy an appreciable amount of material, but when it is remembered that there may be thousands of individual insects to the square metre, it has to be admitted that these little animals have an important function. Scavenging activity is often confused with the action of phytophagous

143

Blue-bottle (*Calliphora*)

▲ Flesh-fly (*Sarcophaga*)

insects. For example, in a dying tree, besides the species which feed on living wood there are others which start to demolish the parts which are already dead, turning the woody material into humus. Flies and Blue-bottles are undoubtedly dangerous carriers of germs, but it should not be forgotten that they play an important part in nature as scavengers. Guided by their sense of smell and their sight, as good fliers they are among the first to reach decomposing organic materials of what can be described as the unstable type, such as corpses, dung and of course the organic remains of human activity. Despite their vile surroundings many large members of Diptera still have splendid colourings, like the metallic green of Green-bottles (*Lucilia*) and the dark blue of Blue-bottles or Blowflies

▼ Green-bottle (*Lucilia*)

(*Calliphora*). The adults of these insects do not use decomposing organic materials directly, but settle on them simply in order to extract the small amount of liquid they need. Their requirements can also be satisfied by flowers on which they like to settle. However, since this only occurs occasionally,

145

▲ Sacred Scarab

▼ Burying Beetle

Blowflies and Blue-bottles are not important as pollinators, except in exceptional cases when the flowers take on a corpse-like smell to deceive the insects and attract the numbers of them. In places where many cows and horses graze, the excited buzzing of hundreds of flies draws attention to the splashes of dung scattered over the pasture. This may seem a disgusting sight, but it is in fact a scene of intense activity. Not only do flies settle on dung to leave their larvae there, but many beetles too take it as their chosen environment. These are, above all, the squat beetles of the families Scarabaeidae and Hydrophilidae, red and black in colour and often with metallic glints. They hurry to fresh dung, the first to arrive being certain Hydrophylids with red markings. Different species then arrive *en masse*: some settle in the dung, others break up the material and bury it. Those which install themselves in the dung include many small hydrophilid beetles and scarabs of the genus *Aphodius*. The Scarabs also include some of the best known insects, foremost among them the sacred scarab. Its deep black colour, dentate forelegs, very long hind legs and shovel-shaped head, dentate like the legs, are its identifying characteristics. Its habit of rolling a ball of dung has been observed since ancient times, arousing such curiosity that the beetle even acquired divine status among the Egyptians. Its care for its offspring, however, has only been noted much more recently. The female buries a ball of dung, but she does not simply lay her eggs in it. Using her legs and head as tools she moulds it into a pear shape, leaving a hollow in the elongated part in which she lays the egg. The larva is an extraordinary shape, with a hump full of faeces on its back. Another dung-rolling beetle, related to the Sacred Scarab, lives near the sea where it is found in sand dunes along the coast. Many of the scarabs found in dung have strange processes, horns and tubercles adorning their head and thorax. These are characteristics of the male and are particularly splendid in members of the genera *Copris* and *Ontophagus*; the first have a curved horn in the middle of the head, the second two small slender horns on the sides of the head, like the horns of cows in tropical regions. Some members of the Silphidae family feed on the dead bodies of animals. They are known as burying or sexton beetles because they locate a dead animal by smell and burrow underneath the corpse until it is covered with soil. The beetles feed on the flesh and also lay their eggs on the corpse, eventually leaving their larvae with a good source of food, safely buried underground.

## Some special tastes

Insects eat everything, as is clear throughout this account of insects' feeding habits.

However, there is an assortment of insects which feed on materials so strange and rare that one really wonders why they didn't choose something else. In fact, these are the great specialists of nature. To avoid competition they have chosen the hardest way, rejecting easy and abundant alternatives. And if it is hard work for the clothes moth seeking out dead animal hair, it is even harder for its intestine which has to digest the keratin the hairs contain.

A dried insect transfixed by a pin in a naturalist's collection seems an unlikely source of food. Yet the little *Anthrenus* beetles of the family Dermestidae do indeed feed on dried insects, and are a real scourge of entomological collections. When they have finished only dust remains of the carefully preserved and perhaps extremely valuable specimen. Other insects with a taste for naturalists' collecting cases and found too in old books are the members of the small order Psocoptera or Book-lice. They do less damage, as on the whole they merely nibble at the glue used to fix the smallest specimens to cards. Another strange diet is that of moths like the wax moth *Galleria mellonella*, which feeds on bees' wax.

The ultimate example for its curiosity value is the species of Bostrichid Beetle, which has been known to attack and damage the lead sheathing of telephone cables.

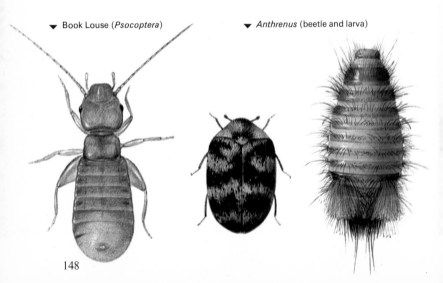

▼ Book Louse (*Psocoptera*)    ▼ *Anthrenus* (beetle and larva)

149

### Different feeding habits of larvae and adults

Although this topic has already been touched on several times, the various aspects of this common insect phenomenon need drawing together. There are many differences between the feeding habits of larvae and adults, deriving from the different functions of the two stages of development. It is worth examining some of the commonest cases. Many species live in the soil in the larval stage, but on plants as adults. This is true of Cicadas. The larvae are equipped with modified forelegs for cutting and digging to make their way between roots in the ground. The adult Cicadas are found on plants and use their rostrum to extract juice.

A similar cycle occurs in Cock-chafer larvae and a number of other scarab beetles which are soil living as larvae, but then transfer to the leaves of trees and flowers. Another frequent difference is between larvae which feed on the solid parts of plants (leaves, stalks and roots) and adults which take only liquid nourishment, especially nectar. This is of course what happens with Moths and Butterflies, but it occurs elsewhere too, especially in Hymenoptera and Diptera. The large Death's Head Hawk Moth of the family Sphingidae is an interesting case. The larva lives on plants, while the adult has an unusually short, strong probiscis so that it can bore through honeycomb in a beehive and steal the honey.

Cockchafer and larva ▾ ▶

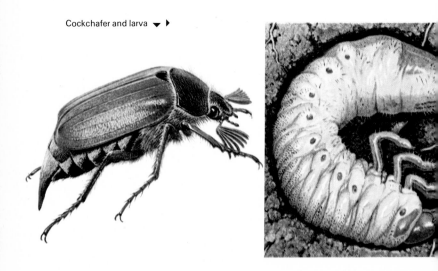

▲ Death's Head
Hawk Moth

▲ Larva of a
Hawk Moth

## Defence: Insects' weapons

Animals can only survive if they are able to defend themselves against enemies. Their defence may be active or passive. Passive methods will be discussed later; this section examines how insects fight actively. They have various weapons, simple and sophisticated. The most obvious but by no means the least effective is a good set of mandibles (jaws). Many carnivores defend themselves by biting, like the Carabidae, spraying their attacker with evil-smelling liquid. In the soldier caste of Termites the mandibles are sometimes highly developed as alarming weapons, with no food-catching function at all.

The abdominal cerci may also have a defensive purpose, as

▼ Bombadier Beetle                    Head of a Soldier Termite ▶

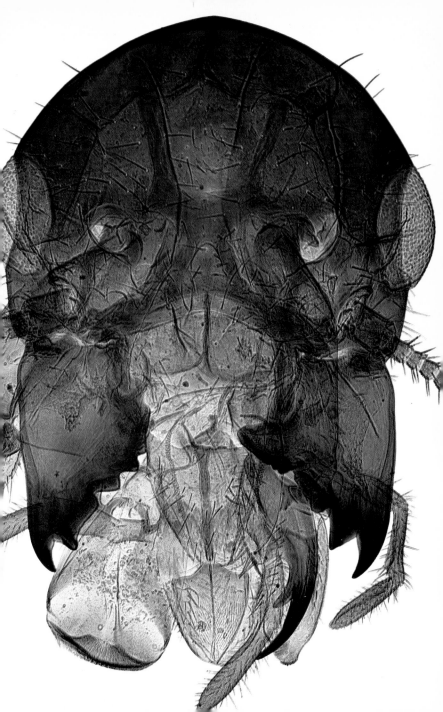

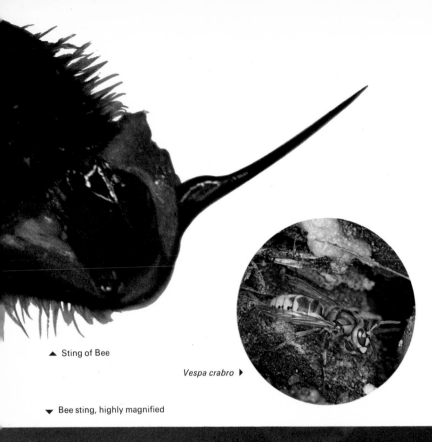

▲ Sting of Bee

*Vespa crabro* ▶

▼ Bee sting, highly magnified

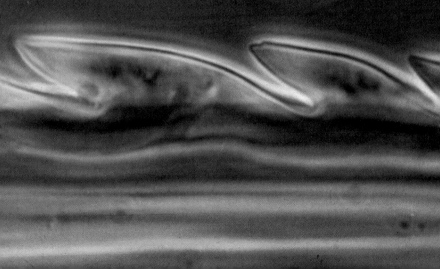

for example in Earwigs, which when disturbed raise the abdomen and try to grasp their attacker with the pincer formed by the cerci. The defence mechanism is usually fairly crude and ineffective, but insects have far more sophisticated weapons. The genus *Brachinus* of the family Carabidae, known as Bombardier Beetles, eject a cloud of gas from the abdomen with a little pop. This is enough to deter any ill-intentioned animal planning to make a meal of the insect. The sting of Hymenoptera, as most of us know to our cost, constitutes a most effective weapon of defence.

Some Diptera, like Mosquitoes and Horseflies, can bite too, but they would never think of using their piercing mouth parts for defence. A startled Horsefly thinks of escaping not attacking. But Hymenoptera are another matter. They know the power of their weapons and make proper use of them. Their sting is really a modified ovipositor, made up of two blades, which are sometimes finely barbed, so that the sting cannot be withdrawn but remains in the body of the victim. However the sting is not always left behind and in many species can be withdrawn undamaged. The sting is connected with a poison system consisting of a canal along which the secretions of two glands, one alkaline, one acid, are pumped. As the sting is a modified ovipositor, obviously only females are able to sting. In this part of the world the most painful sting is that inflicted by the Hornet (*Vespula crabro*), a large wasp which nests inside tree trunks.

## Warning coloration

Everybody must at some time during the summer months have noticed on flowers curious little red and black moths, gaudily coloured and quite unable to escape. If disturbed they allow themselves to be captured easily and do not seem too worried about it. Such behaviour is quite remarkable: what makes these insects so self-assured? One possible explanation emerges if one takes a sniff at the insect, which has a fairly strong odour.

Numerous experiments have shown that it is completely uneatable so far as its most dangerous potential enemies, birds, are concerned. The gaudy colour is the means by which the insect defends itself: it acts as an alarm signal to any animal which might want to eat it. Of course a bird does not instinctively know the risk involved in eating a *Zygaena*, as these little moths are known, and it must therefore undergo at least once the experience of vomiting after eating one.

▼ Zygaena Moth          ▼ Caterpillar of *Cerura* (Puss Moth)

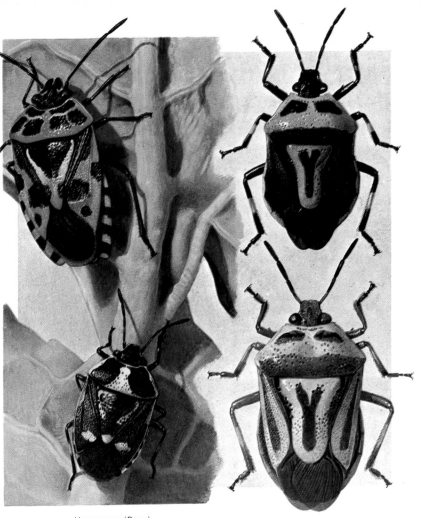

▲ Heteroptera (Bugs)

The sacrifice of one moth would be enough to ensure the survival of many others. Moreover, if a bird happened to peck a *Zygaena* it is soft enough not to come to harm. Warning coloration is very common in insects and is found, for example, in many brightly-coloured foetid-smelling heteropterans.

### Cryptic mimicry

In nature, an animal which is good to eat cannot allow itself the luxury of a handsome appearance and brilliant colouring: such folly would be rewarded with death. Many insects are therefore masters in the art of disguise and cryptic mimicry – a resemblance to something else so that it cannot be seen.

One whole order, Phasmida, specializes in this type of mimicry, resulting in the seemingly paradoxical forms of its members. The Stick Insects are the most famous. The exotic species are up to twelve inches (thirty centimetres) long and look exactly like sticks, their long slender legs only serving to confuse matters further. A moving twig would lose credibility and so these insects almost always remain motionless. Many

▼ Stick Insect

▼ Leaf Insect

▲ Grasshopper with camouflage marking

species do not have wings, or only wings which function badly. However, the second pair may be brightly coloured in order to distract possible attackers. The Leaf Insects of the hotter regions must be mentioned, together with the Stick Insects. These flat green insects, which have wings so like leaves that they even have ribbing, perhaps represent the highest level of cryptic mimicry. Colour is as important as form in the mimicry of these insects. Some Stick Insects are brown, others green, in imitation of the two commonest plant colours: sometimes an ability to change colour – extremely rare in insects – has been observed.

In Homoptera, the mimicry of many Tree-hoppers of the family Membracidae is interesting. These insects have long processes, surprisingly like thorns. Another striking example is provided by some African Cicadelidae or Leaf Hoppers which settle on stems in groups and, taken together, look like a cluster of flowers. A resemblance to the insect's surroundings may deceive potential victims as well as predators. This is true of mantids, which because of their form and colour blend

159

▲ Camouflage of *Cucullia* caterpillar

exceptionally well with green foliage. Thanks to its pink
colouring and particular shape one Maltese mantid is able to
lie in wait among orchid flowers of the same hue. One might
assume that Moths and Butterflies, because of their showy
colouring and form, could hardly be described as insects which
blend with their environment. However, their caterpillars,
which are not able to escape, often use mimicry as their sole
means of defence. The Geometridae caterpillar's curious
looping forward movement has already been described. Faced
by danger, it grips firmly with its abdominal prolegs and

▲ Caterpillar of Geometrid moth

reaches stiffly out into the air; as it is bark-coloured with little protuberances like the surface of a tree it looks just the same as a dry twig.

Notodontidae caterpillars have odd bulges on their body so that they readily resemble bits of wood, dry leaves or other parts of the tree they live on. Another caterpillar provides a particularly subtle form of imitation: with brown markings on its green body it resembles the withering flowers of the Compositae, on which it lives. Finally, in a great many species imitation simply involves homochromy or identical colouring.

For example, there are many caterpillars exactly the same green as the leaves they attack.

Adult Butterflies do not seem at all mimetic. Their bright colours, large wings and almost impudent splendour suggest reckless vanity. This is quite untrue. These butterflies can camouflage themselves most effectively. To understand how it is necessary to examine, firstly, the way in which their wings are held at rest. Many species always keep them vertically closed when they settle; others keep them half or fully open, but are ready to close them at the slightest suspicious noise. The two sides of each wing must now be considered. The gaudy colours – bright red and glowing blue – are confined to the side of the wing seen from above when the insect has its wings open. The

male

◀ ▼ Camouflage of a nocturnal moth

female

Grayling Butterfly

underside is quite different. The hind wings are often densely patterned areas of bright colour, alternating with dull patches. The forewings may be coloured underneath as well, but a small part at the wing tip will be nondescript in colour, like the hind wing. When the butterfly has its wings closed and is disturbed it will draw the forewings between the hindwings, leaving only the protectively coloured part showing. In this way the butterfly is scarcely visible, particularly as, when seen from the front, the closed wings are so slight as to be unnoticeable Moths at rest keep their wings in a roof shape over their back. The forewings have mimetic coloration like bark or rock, but the hindwings may be very gaudy, as in genera *Catocala* and *Triphaena* of the family Noctuidae.

Camouflage of
tterflies

Peacock butterfly
*Inachis io*

163

**Imitation: Batesian and Mullerian mimicry**

Insects, as we know, have more or less effective weapons to defend themselves: a species well equipped in this way is feared and respected. Similarly, insects which have a repellent or even poisonous taste will not get eaten easily. Species which display these characteristics are protected against many dangers, and it frequently happens that insects without these defences imitate the form, colour and movement of the other insects, behaving as mimics to arouse fear by trickery. This type of mimicry is described as Batesian. Hymenoptera supply some of the favourite models for imitation, because of their sting which is known and feared by many other animals as well as man. *Eristalis*, a quite harmless Hoverfly, closely resembles a Bee. When the poet Virgil said Bees were born from meat he was very likely mistakenly referring to these insects, the larvae of which do live in putrified liquids.

Wasps are another group of Hymenoptera with many imitations. If we see an insect with a yellow and black striped

▼ Hoverfly (*Eristalis*)

▼ Bee

abdomen we immediately assume it is a wasp, but it may well be a syrphid fly or even a moth. In moths of the family Sesiidae the wings are only partly covered with scales and the abdomen is often striped yellow and black. They look incredibly like wasps, and only the expert is not taken in.

Ants have their imitators too, especially among the insects which frequent their nests, but the purpose of this resemblance is not really understood. Mimicry may involve movements and attitudes as well as form and colour. One insect may copy the position which another adopts to emit poisonous substances, without itself producing anything. This is enough to put off enemies.

Some Butterflies imitate more than one model. A single species may include individuals which resemble different uneatable species. The African butterfly *Papilio dardanus* displays in the females an incredible range of mimetic forms which differ according to the various races into which the species is split over its distribution area.

▼ Harmless flies (on right) which imitate Hymenoptera (left)

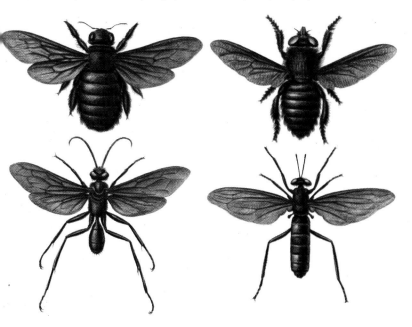

A very similar type of mimicry involves resemblance between different uneatable species. This is known as Mullerian mimicry, and is effective because the advantages are shared by two or more species at once. A predator which has an unpleasant experience with one species will automatically reject the other as well, and so the second species will not have to lose too many of its own individuals before the predator learns to reject them. The fact that there is just one model reduces the total losses.

A simple example of Mullerian mimicry is provided by moths of the families Ctenuchidae and Zygaenidae, which are common in Europe, though the most outstanding examples occur among South American fauna in the families Heliconiidae and Ithomiidae which have long brightly coloured wings. Looking at a collection case of these insects it is easy to group them on the basis of wing pattern, as there are not many variations of coloration. However, a careful

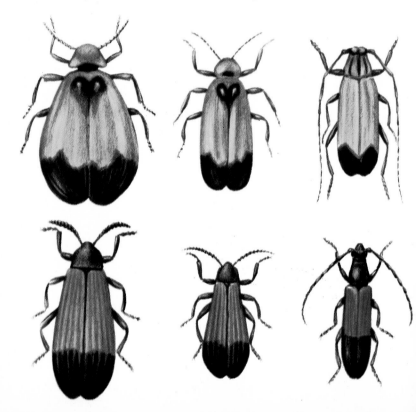

examination of specimens which seem the same will show little differences making two, three or four different species, which have the same colouring but differ as regards characteristics like wing venation which really show the relationships between species. At times the imitations are so complex, that the naturalist cannot grasp their logic or give an objective explanation of the phenomenon.

These two types of mimicry, Batesian and Mullerian, are not mutually exclusive but interact in series of similar species, even belonging to different orders, which form what are known as mimicry rings. The first series illustrated shows from the left the male and female of *Lycus rostratus*, a Lycid beetle; *Amphidesmus analis*, a Cerambycid beetle; the heteropteran *Lygaeus fureatus*; the lepidopteran *Neurosyphoea ochreipennis*; the hymenopteran *Pompilus capensis*. These insects all live in South Africa. The other series illustrated shows a similar ring found in Borneo. Page 169 shows three rings consisting entirely

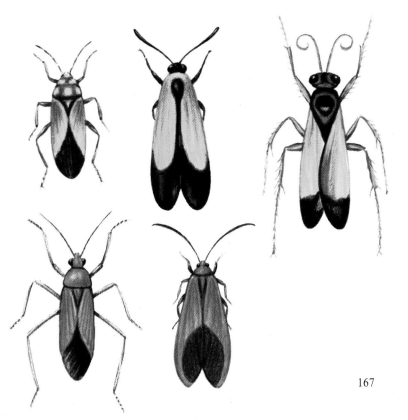

of Butterflies of different families. In each series a horizontal line separates the uneatable species (above) from the eatable (below). The mimicry adopted by the species above the line is Mullerian, since it involves insects which are all protected by their own poison system; those below the line are examples of Batesian mimicry.

Mimicry does not just involve insects: a plant may do the deceiving and the insect may be deceived. In many plants of the Orchideae family part of the flower resembles in shape and colour the female of some species of Hymenoptera. The male tries to mate with this deceptive image and in so doing involuntarily collects the flower's pollen, contained in pollen sacs, which sticks to his head and is carried to another flower. In this way the cross-fertilization necessary for the survival of the species occurs.

It is very easy to see the question of mimicry in a false light. Above all, it is important not to think of imitation as intentional or to imagine that the insect knows it resembles a poisonous insect or is the same colour as its surroundings. The insect knows nothing about mimicry and in any case has no way of assuming colours, which are determined entirely by heredity. So how is the appearance of mimics to be explained? There is one famous example which may be helpful. The Peppered Moth (*Biston betularia*), of the family Geometridae, exists in two different forms. In one the wings are white with irregular dark markings, in the other they are dark all over. In colour the pale form resembles Birch bark and it is almost invisible when it settles on a Birch tree. Before the Industrial Revolution in England the pale form definitely predominated, but at a certain point the situation changed. Tree trunks, especially Birch trees, became coated with smoke and soot from the new industries and the pale colour of the white form of *Biston* showed up glaringly on these surfaces. Predators then concentrated their attentions on the pale form which soon became very rare.

This kind of explanation is of course only a deduction and does not rule out the possibility that other factors may have affected the increase of the dark type. However, there is much evidence to support the hypothesis which seems readily acceptable, at least in its broad outlines.

Thus selection is the decisive factor which favours mimetic individuals given the pitiless logic by which the fittest survive.

There is probably more mimicry than we know, involving not only colours and forms but also odour which may or may not be perceptible to man.

Batesian and Mullerian mimicry in several Butterflies ▶

▲ Nest and eggs of Mole Cricket

▼ Parasitic Braconid

▼ Braconid pupae on caterpillar of Cabbage White Butterfly

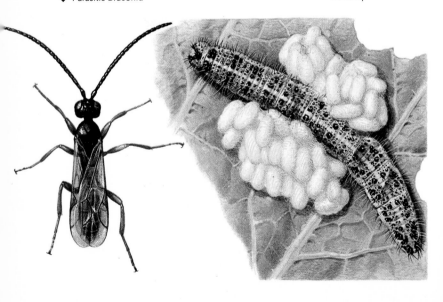

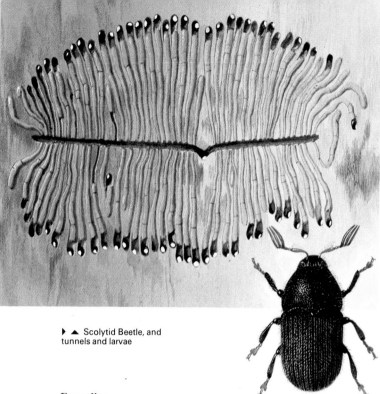

▶ ▲ Scolytid Beetle, and
tunnels and larvae

**Fecundity**

For all their weapons and tricks, insects face a thousand
dangers and survival is an undertaking in which only a few
succeed. Too many animals live off them and hunger sharpens
their wits. The stomach of birds, reptiles, amphibians and
mammals is where some insects always meet their end. At this
level survival is not something which can be solved by
individuals: it is a mass problem.

An increase in the number of individuals making up a
population increases correspondingly the chances that some
will survive to perpetuate the species.

It is to this end that insects are so alarmingly prolific and
thus overcome the problem of the gradual decimation of their
numbers. Different animals are responsible for the massacre.
The eggs are in danger and even when protected by oothecae
these are attacked by many small parasites. The larvae are the
most exposed. They must beware of both small animals (insects
and mites) and large ones (birds). The adult is usually better
equipped, but often succumbs to birds and to the spider which
excels in the capture of flying prey.

171

# Associations

Imagine a meadow high up in the mountains, a spot where the sun and weather have scattered a stretch of green grass with stones from the gradual crumbling of the rock. It is spring and there are still patches of snow on the ground. Given the melting snow, there is of course also a stream. The simplest way to start a search for insects in this spot is by turning over stones. Dazzled by the light many little animals will scatter in confusion. A close look will reveal an unexpected fact. The area under examination, which may have seemed quite uniform, at different points shelters associations of different insects. Near the snow there will be species which will not be found in the parts where

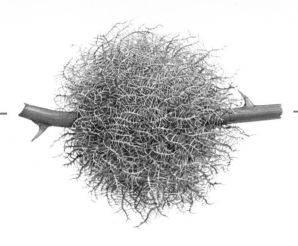

the grass has already grown. There are different insects there, and yet others by the stream.

A study carried out in a less selected spot, with more favourable environmental conditions than the mountains, would reveal even more diverse associations of insects dependent on the many micro-environments.

The distribution and association of insects is thus a fascinating field for study from either a purely scientific or a strictly practical point of view. If the entomologist can understand what any given insect's real requirements are he can, in the case of harmful species, plan the most effective methods to fight them.

▲ Bumble bee pollinating
a Labiate flower

### Insects and plants

Without insects the higher plants – the flowering plants which
grow on dry land – could not exist. Between these two groups
of living things there is a vital link, a complex relationship
which might be described as one of love and death.

The positive side of the relationship is the work of
pollination which many insects perform. The flowers have a
whole range of mechanisms to attract insects and scatter them
with the fertilizing pollen. It would be pleasant to think that the
flowers' dazzling colours and scents are there to gladden the
heart of man in springtime, but they are aimed at insects. Inside
the flower there are devices of varying degrees of complexity
designed to make the pollen stick to the insect's body.

And so without insects most plants could not reproduce.
When European clover was taken to Australia it did not thrive

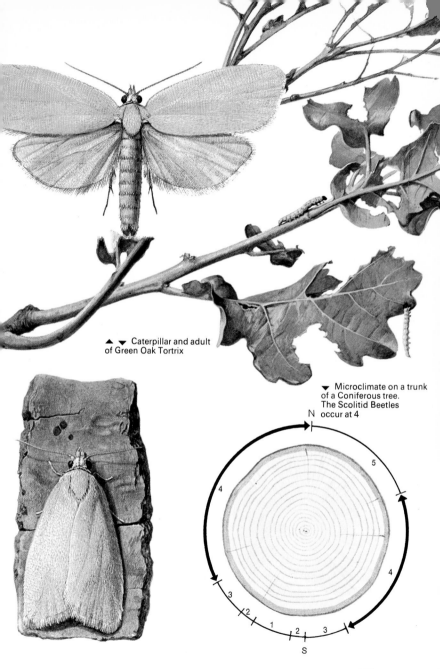

▲ ▼ Caterpillar and adult of Green Oak Tortrix

▼ Microclimate on a trunk of a Coniferous tree. The Scolitid Beetles occur at 4

N

S

175

until the Bumble Bees responsible for its fertilization were also introduced. Besides the insects which specialize in pollinating plants there are large numbers which exploit them. From its roots to its topmost branches a tree shelters many species, each making use of a different part – wood, leaves, fruit and seeds. Moreover, although one might assume that a leaf-eating or a wood-eating insect could settle on any part of the tree, this is not so. Some beetles of the Scolytidae family which live under the bark of conifers will only settle in parts which are exposed in a particular way (in the illustration on page 175 they are indicated by a number 4). In other parts of the bark the

▼ Cetoniid Beetle

exposure and therefore the climate are such that the insect cannot survive. They are distributed irregularly in a way directly determined by the different micro-climates which exist around and inside the tree.

The appearance of various species of insect attacker on a plant is also distributed in time, from early species which appear in spring to late ones in autumn. This is because each phytophagous insect needs to find a plant at a particular moment in its annual cycle. *Anthonomous pomorum*, a small

Weevil which attacks apple trees, appears very early in spring, when it completes its cycle of development in the flower.

Insects attack plants in different ways. The simplest method of gnawing directly the leaves, wood or other parts of the plant has been discussed at length in the sections on feeding habits. Many insects are sap-suckers and have a snout or rostrum which pierces the tissues to reach the sap. Many species produce special substances which act on plants to produce abnormal growth of the tissues. These form variously shaped excrescenses or galls inside which the insect lives. Species of many different groups cause these galls. Many Aphids are

▼ Nymph of Froghopper

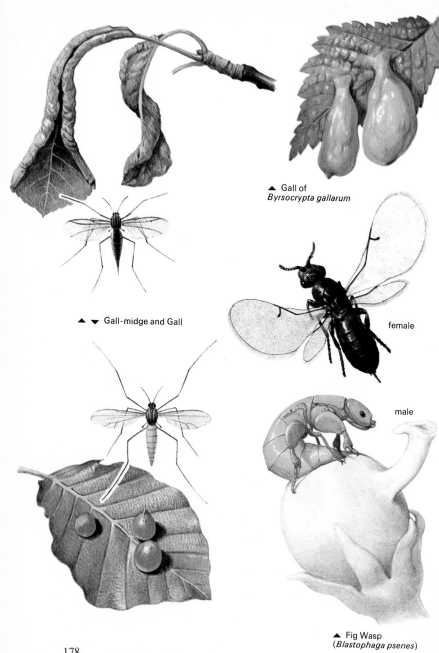

▲ Gall of
*Byrsocrypta gallarum*

▲ ▼ Gall-midge and Gall

female

male

▲ Fig Wasp
(*Blastophaga psenes*)

178

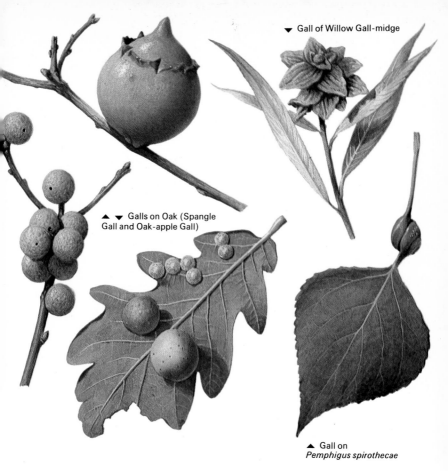

▼ Gall of Willow Gall-midge

▲ ▼ Galls on Oak (Spangle
Gall and Oak-apple Gall)

▲ Gall on
*Pemphigus spirothecae*

responsible for them. You may have seen pouch-like galls on
elm leaves produced by *Byrsocrypta gallarum* and those
affecting the petioles of poplar leaves, the work of the Aphid
*Pemphigus spirothecae*. Inside these galls many insects live,
immersed in a powdery mass of wax. Galls produced by
members of Hymenoptera are very large and solid and often
almost spherical like those produced by the Gall Wasps *Cynips
quercustozae* and *Cynips kollari* of the family Cynipidae.
*Rhodites rosae* produces galls covered with filaments. In
Diptera, the Gall-midges of the family Cecidomyidae produce
different shaped and coloured galls.

The Fig Wasp of the family Agaonidae of Hymenoptera are
of great interest. They produce a gall inside flowers, performing
a very useful fertilization job at the same time.

179

Insects behave as if they were in control on plants, but here, as elsewhere, they are surrounded by danger. Danger from other insects, from other animals and from the plants themselves. On flowers, for example, little spiders are often lying in wait – crab-shaped and delicately coloured like the petals they live on. These members of the family Homisidae catch their prey without a web and are expert in ambush. Insectivorous plants such as the sundew snare unwary insects with sticky secretions.

▲ Diplura

▲ Staphylinid Beetle

### Soil-living insects

During the autumn a mass transfer of plant material takes place in deciduous woods. As the leaves fall, they carry to the ground the energy which plants store in their organic compounds. What was the food-supply of leaf-eating insects is taken from them and passed over to the destructive band living in the soil.

What do insects find to eat in the soil? Decomposing plant material firstly, and then a large amount of material from fungi, including both the fruit-bearing body and the mass of filaments which make up the mycelium. There is also food for many predators and parasites. A food chain is thus formed, based on dead rather than living plants, and having as its links many animals which specialize in the same way as those which live on green plants. In other words, here too there are peaceful plant-feeders, aggressive predators and stealthy parasites.

However, soil-living insects do not dominate their environment in the same way as insects living on leaves and grass. Competition is fierce. Scavengers in the soil include enormous numbers of little Acari or Mites, with eight legs as a reminder that they belong to the Arachnida. Then there are the many-legged animals: the Millipedes, members of Diplopoda, which slowly eat debris and the agile Centipedes belonging to

▲ Thysanuran (Machilid)

▼ Protura

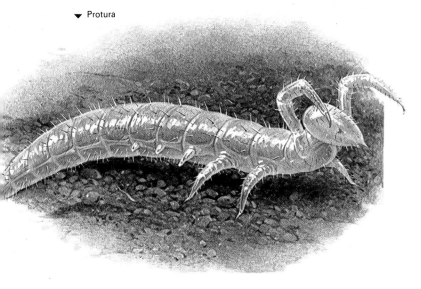

183

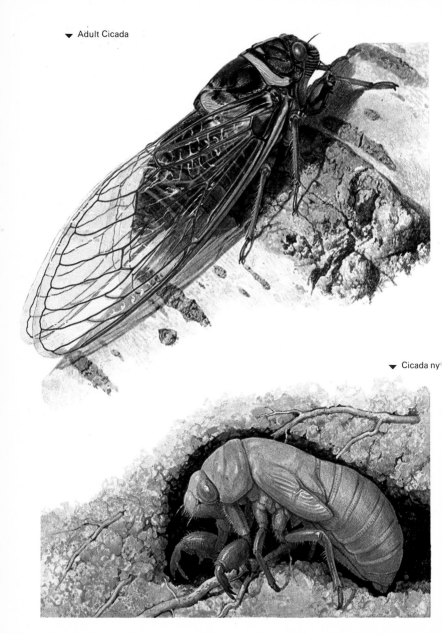

▼ Adult Cicada

▼ Cicada ny

184

Chilopoda; the large *Scolopendria* looking like tank tracks, the long *Geophilus* and the swift *Lithobius*. There are many members of the Annelida, from Earth Worms to the little Enchytraeidae, many Isopod crustaceans, grey, white or pink in colour, and so on to the lowly Nematodes and Rotifers which survive on drops of water in the soil. It is interesting that members of all the insect orders considered to be most primitive live in the soil – that is to say those which do not have wings, and never have had any in the course of evolution. The rare Protura are found there, insects so strange and unusual that some zoologists refuse to class them as insects at all. They have no eyes, and, very unusually, no antennae. They have twelve abdominal segments, the largest number of any insect. They hold their forelegs up in a curious way so that they act as substitute antennae. Another group of primitive soil-living insects are the pale-coloured Diplura, which can move agilely and quickly. In some of these insects, the abdomen ends in a pair of long, slender cerci, while in others these appendages are short and strong. Many Staphylined beetles, a much more evolved class of insects, have a similar body structure and so are just as agile and able to get into cracks and crevices. As already mentioned, a great many members of Collembola, another primitive order, are soil-living. Finally, there is the humpback family Machilidae of order Thysanura. The layer of soil in which insects live is not the same throughout. The upper part is rich in plant detritus and quite different from the lower layer, where there are only root ends and a very limited supply of organic material.

The insects which live on the various levels are as a result very different. Near the surface there are many agile species, often with functional wings and well-developed eyes, which can move away as they need to. Further down come the specialized insects, which have no pigment, reduced eyes or even none, and which are sometimes very slow in movement. Little is known about them, not even what they eat or what their larvae look like. Insects of this type, known as Endogaea, are particularly common in chalky soil which has plenty of cracks, allowing the insects to move about a certain amount. These insects include the lowly Leptotiphlinae, Staphylinids less than a millimetre long and which are common in the Mediterranean region. Formerly unknown species are constantly being discovered, but the difficulties involved, given their tiny size and slow movements, mean there are many species to be found.

Catching these tiny insects takes patience, skill and experience, and the use of special techniques.

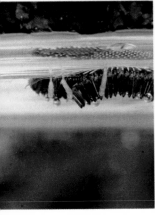

▲ Mosquito eggs

▲ Mosquito pupa

▲ Adult and larva of *Anopheles*

▼ Mosquito adult

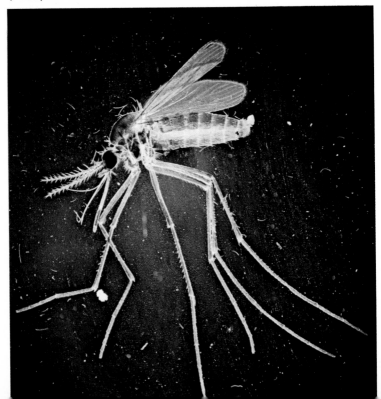

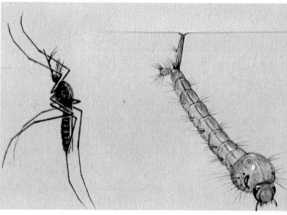

▲ Adult and larva of *Culex*

### Aquatic insects

Insects cannot live in the sea and only a very few members of Hemiptera brave salt water. In fresh water, however, they are present in large numbers, despite considerable competition from other invertebrates such as Crustaceans, Annelids, Molluscs and many others.

Obviously, the insect's first problem is respiration and the oxygen supply, since variable amounts of oxygen may be dissolved in the water, or, in other words, the water may be more or less oxygenated. Sometimes, the insect overcomes this difficulty in the simplest way by continuing to breathe atmospheric oxygen. The insect has to surface periodically to breathe, or has a syphon which reaches up to the air. Other species have a special breathing system involving, instead of the usual tracheae, gills or tracheal gills so that it can breathe oxygen dissolved in the water. Species which breathe atmospheric oxygen are incompletely aquatic, but those which breathe dissolved oxygen are true aquatics. Some insects spend their whole life in water, others only pass the larval stage there, but even species linked to the water at all stages of development can leave it, since they never lose their capacity for flight.

A well-known water-insect is undoubtedly the Mosquito, a familiar torment of summer nights. These two-winged insects are members of Diptera and related to flies. There are various species of Mosquito, found especially in hotter parts of the world. Only two will be discussed : Culicines and Anophelines.

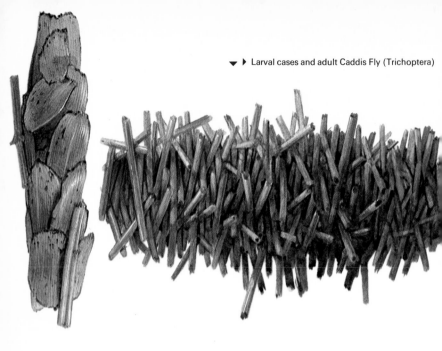

▼ ▶ Larval cases and adult Caddis Fly (Trichoptera)

It should be made clear from the start that in both groups only the females are blood suckers. The male, easily distinguished by its long plumose antennae, only feeds on sugary substances. While the bite of the ordinary Culicine mosquito may be painful, the bite of Anophelines is also notoriously dangerous, since it can transmit malaria. It is easy to tell the two species apart by their resting positions. The Culicine mosquito keeps its body parallel to the surface on which it is resting, while *Anopheles* keeps its body raised so that the head points down. There are differences, too, in the position of the larvae under the surface film of the water. The body of the Culicine mosquito is held at a 45° angle to the surface, while *Anopheles* stays parallel to the surface, just under the surface film. In the larval stage these insects feed on floating microscopic organisms, especially algae and protozoa. They are incompletely aquatic, since they breathe atmospheric oxygen through a short syphon. The gradual elimination of malaria in many parts of the world is explained by the fact that the Anopheline larva is so much more particular than the Culicine mosquito and will only live in oxygenated water. Its distribution is therefore confined to areas where these conditions are found and so it is not as widespread as the Culicine mosquito, which lives more or less anywhere.

188

189

Another group of insects which have an amphibious life-cycle are Trichoptera or Caddis Flies. The adults are very like Butterflies and have wings covered by hairs, and even a few scales. The larvae, however, are aquatic and have the curious habit of building themselves cases from bits of plant, pebbles and even empty snail shells, all stuck together with silk. The

▲ Mayfly

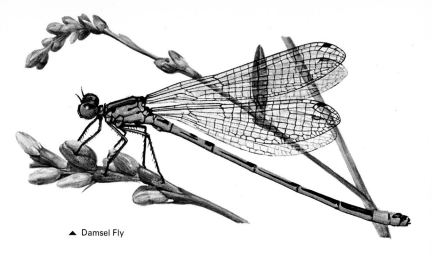

▲ Damsel Fly

case is open at both ends and only the head and thorax protrude, so that the insect can readily withdraw in case of danger. These cases not only protect the insect, but help to prevent its being carried off by the current. Trichoptera live in streams and often build their cases with pebbles which add considerably to their weight. In calm water pebbles are scarce, but they are not needed as the insects are not in danger of being carried away by the current.

Ephemeroptera (Mayflies), Odonata (Dragonflies and Damselflies) and Plecoptera (Stoneflies), the three most primitive insect orders with aquatic larvae, have already been mentioned several times. It is worth adding, however, that in Ephemeroptera there are several distinct types of larvae which differ in structure depending on their environment. Some calm water species can swim; others move along the slimy depths; those living under stones in swift-flowing water have flattened

▼ Stonefly

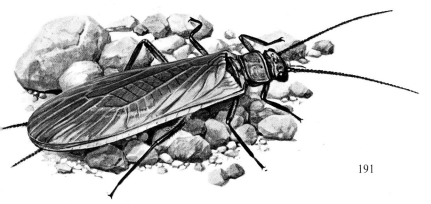

191

bodies; and finally there are some species which burrow galleries in the waterbed. Some Mayflies and many Stoneflies can only live in very clean, well-oxygenated water, so their presence or absence may show whether a river is polluted or not.

▼ Aquatic Beetles: (1) Whirly-gig Beetle; (2) Great Silver Water Beetle and larva; (3) Great Water Beetle male; (4) Great Water Beetle female; (5) Great Water Beetle larva

▲ Water Beetle with air supply

The insects which spend their whole life in water are members of Coleoptera and Heteroptera. Both types are incompletely aquatic and breathe atmospheric oxygen; they therefore take a supply of air with them while immersed. The Dytiscidae beetles, for example, move around with a bubble of air attached to their abdomen. These insects often have special hairs to carry air. *Dytiscus* is one of the Water-beetles best adapted for swimming. Its oval stream-lined body is perfect for moving through the water, propelled by the hindlegs which have flattened tarsi and stiff bristles. The larva can be found near the adult. It is an ugly creature, fierce-looking because of its long sickle-like mandibles which not only catch prey but also contain a hollow channel along which food is sucked; the food cannot pass through the mouth which is kept closed.

The Great Silver Water-beetle, *Hydrophilus piceus*, is, at two inches (five centimetres) long, our largest Water-beetle. It has distinctive, highly developed maxillary palps which could be mistaken for antennae. Its hindlegs have the same flattened form as *Dytiscus* although it is not such a good swimmer. Whereas all members of the family Dytiscidae have a perfectly shaped body for moving through water, the Hydrophilids are often not adapted in form for swimming and move slowly on the bottom, under stones and along submerged plants.

On the surface of the water we find the small, very fast Whirligig Beetles of the family Gyrinidae. Their paddle-like hind legs are even more specialized in form than those of *Dytiscus*. However, unlike *Dytiscus* the Whirligig Beetles usually swim on the surface of the water, rather than in it, whirling around in endless arabesques. Their eyes are unusual in that they are divided into two, the top portion being used for vision out of the water, the bottom for vision in it. Other European water beetles include some members of the families Haliplidae and Dryopidae, the former distinguished by their long legs, the latter by their slow movements and the fine hairs which cover many species.

The Nepidae are curious water bugs. The wide flattened body and reptatorial forelegs of *Nepa cinerea* bear a certain resemblance to a scorpion. The similarity is underlined by an appendage at the end of the abdomen which looks like a scorpion's 'tail'. In fact, this is the syphon the insect uses to breathe atmospheric oxygen. A similar appendage occurs in *Ranatra*, a long and slender insect very like the pond skaters.

▼ Whirlygig Beetles

▼ Aquatic Hemiptera: (1) Pond Skater; (2) Water Measurer; (3) Water Boatman; (4) Water Scorpion; (5) Water Stick-insect

195

▼ Nest of the
Processionary
Moth Caterpillar

▲ Pine Processionary Moth

**Gregarious insects**

In pine woods it is often possible to see whitish masses hanging from branches. These are the nests of Processionary Moths, which as caterpillars lead a gregarious life.

Countless insects associate at some stage of their life. Sometimes the relationship between members of a colony is more than just neighbourly. Take the processionaries. There are Oak Processionaries, as well as the pine species. As adults they are insignificant, pale-coloured moths. As larvae their behaviour is remarkable. With silk threads they build roomy shelters which they leave at night in orderly ranks which form terrible destructive processions and wreak havoc on the leaves of the host tree. Sometimes, the band is made up not of a single file of insects, but of a widening formation in which one caterpillar is followed by two more, then three and so on. Obviously, such behaviour depends on precise mechanisms, not on chance. Each caterpillar is induced to follow the one immediately in front by a tactile stimulus when its head touches the hairs on the tip of the abdomen, and also by the trail of silk left by the caterpillars further on in the line. The procession can only consist of individuals from the same batch of eggs. Processionary caterpillars are also well known for violent skin irritation their touch can cause.

▼ Processionary Caterpillars

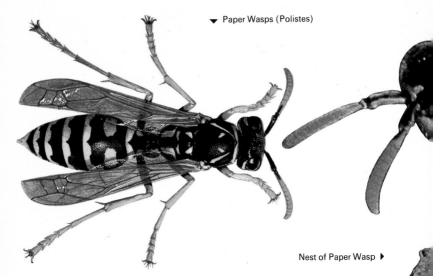

Paper Wasps (Polistes)

Nest of Paper Wasp ▶

### Societies

Before discussing social insects it is necessary first to define what exactly is meant by societies in the insect world. They differ from other associations between members of a population, because of the division of tasks between individuals. Reproduction is always limited to a very small number of individuals, and usually there is only one fertile female. The males play a very small part in community life, often confined to mating. The majority of the society's members are sterile individuals, which simply satisfy food and defence requirements. Associations may be more or less complex, and may be small in size or made up of countless individuals. Wasp societies are usually fairly simple and so will be examined first.

A good example is the Paper Wasp, *Polistes gallicus*, which is very common on the continent, where its nests are often found under mouldings on sunny house walls. They consist of a certain number of little cells, grouped together and attached to the support by a stalk. The material used seems very like paper and is a pulp made from finely ground wood. The societies of these Wasps are founded in spring with the reunion of several fertile females which have spent the winter hibernating. One of these females gains supremacy and the others are relegated to a subordinate position, and even lose their fertility. These societies are annual, as only a few females survive the winter.

Worker Bee

## Hive Bees

Hive bees are the best known social insects, which is scarcely surprising when one considers their age-old connections with man. They belong to the family Apidae of order Hymenoptera, a family which also includes the Bumble Bees of the species *Bombus*, large social insects with striped hairy bodies which are widely distributed and play an important part in the pollination of flowers. Bees that are kept for honey belong to the species *Apis mellifica*, the only one suitable for this purpose.

There are three distinct castes or types of individuals in bee societies: queens, drones and workers. The queen is the fertile female and is distinguished by the size of the abdomen, which is visibly larger than in the common worker. Although she lays an enormous number of eggs during her long life – she may live up to five years – the queen is only fertilized once, during what is known as the marriage flight. She is able to keep the spermatozoa alive for an exceptionally long period compared with the usually brief life of male reproductive cells. The drones are the males and they are concerned solely with reproduction. They have none of the structures which the workers use to make honey and gather pollen, and so they are not held in so much esteem by the workers, who often eliminate them. The

▼ Queen Bee                                 ▼ Drone

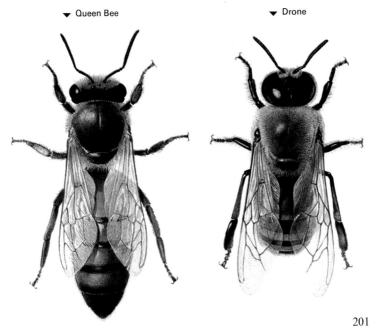

most interesting fact about drones is that they come from unfertilized eggs or, in other words, are produced by parthenogenesis.

The workers are the third caste and represent the vast majority of individuals in any hive. They are female and as their name indicates they are responsible for all the work in the hive. They therefore have faculties denied to the other castes. They can produce honey, gather pollen, make royal jelly and are equipped with a poisonous sting. The workers are completely sterile, although they are definitely female, since they are born from fertilized eggs, unlike the males. Differentiation between them and the queens occurs during the larval stage and depends on the different kind of care given to the larvae. The workers have special glands called the pharyngeal glands which produce royal jelly, a substance fed to all larvae in the first three days of life, but during the next larval stage given only to those which are to become queens. The workers' lives is not a tedious succession of identical days but consists of different periods dedicated to different activities. In the first stage they are mainly occupied inside the nest where to maintain a constant temperature they provide cooling ventilation by beating their wings and warmth by muscular vibration. The second stage is concerned with feeding the larvae, firstly with honey and pollen and then with royal jelly, as the special glands become operative. Next, the workers become able to produce wax and start building cells. The last period of life takes the bee out into the fields to look for flowers. Here the workers exhaust themselves by constant activity, and eventually die.

Nests are built in cavities. They consist of combs two cell layers thick built of wax which is produced by the workers from special glands. The individual cells are hexagonal, the shape best adapted for a rational use of space. They are not all the same size. The queen cells are larger and sac-like. The drone cells are also larger. The formation of a new colony is a rare event, involving the spectacular phenomenon of swarming. In response to certain stimuli, such as the queen's old age, the workers rear some females in special cells, feeding them entirely on royal jelly. As a result queens develop instead of the usual workers. This provokes considerable agitation among the workers. They leave the nest in large numbers and with the old queen settle on some nearby support. After a period of search the swarm, consisting of tens of thousands of individuals, selects a suitable spot for a new nest. At this point a human bee-keeper usually intervenes and transfers the swarm to an

▼ Swarm of Bees

▲ Bees on a flower

Diagram showing the bee dance ▶

artificial hive. Meanwhile, in the old nest, one of the newly-matured queens gains supremacy. The others are suppressed or leave to form other swarms, so that there is always only one queen at the head of the colony.

Like most animal groups, members of insect communities have their own means of communication. The simplest form of communication, common to many social insects, is by pheromones. These are types of hormone which can be secreted by an animal to influence the behaviour of others of its own species. The pheromones stimulate specific functions and are exchanged between individuals. This enables messages to be circulated among the whole community.

Honey bees also have a special means of communication known as the 'bee dance'. The form and speed of a bee's dancing movements will indicate to other bees the whereabouts of a good food supply. The bees use the position of the sun to fix a bearing on the food supply and can even make allowances for the sun's movement during the day.

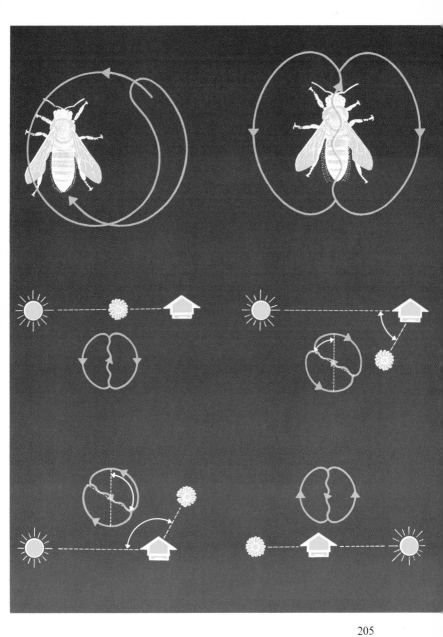

Queen

male

## Ants

Ant societies differ from bee societies in many respects, although they have some basic characteristics in common. There are again three separate castes: males, fertile females (destined to become queens) and workers. The workers are not all the same, unlike worker Bees. Sometimes the caste is divided into sub-castes, and it is often possible to distinguish the workers proper from the soldiers, who have large heads and strong jaws. The division into sub-castes allows the necessary distribution of work which in bees is performed by a single individual at different points in its life. All Ants are social, whereas Social Bees are relatively few compared with the number of solitary species. The ants' nest is a permanent society which may last several years. It is founded in quite a

◀ Nest and adults of *Formica rufa* (Wood Ant)

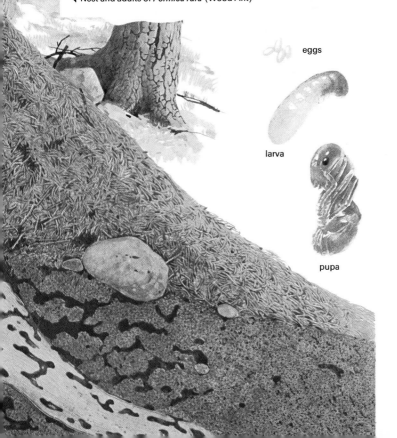

eggs

larva

pupa

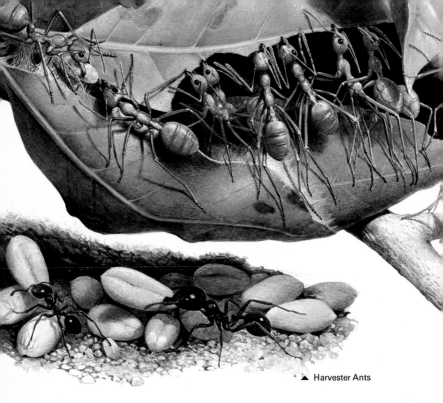

**▲** Harvester Ants

different way from a new beehive. Swarming occurs, but this does not mean the same thing as with Bees. The workers do not take part and are, in any case, wingless. The swarm is a disorderly flight of thousands of males and winged females which leave all the nests in an area at the same time; they mate and then fall exhausted to the ground in large numbers. At this point the males have fulfilled their purpose and die. The females which survive the destructive attacks of predators prepare to found a new colony. Usually, there is a single female founder, acting unaided in the early stages. She breaks off her wings and begins to rear the first workers, using as food either some of her own eggs or the reabsorbed wing muscles which are no longer needed. Only rarely does the queen go out in search of food. Ants' nests are built in all kinds of places. Nests in the grounds consist of a series of communicating chambers. They are often hidden under stones, but sometimes protected by a mound of plant detritus. These ant heaps, which are often found in coniferous wood, can be remarkably tall. Many Ant species settle in trees, especially in ones already decaying, and may form complex galleries there. Others may pick a human habitation where they will certainly never be short of food.

Many Ants are parasites. Some take over the nests of other species by force and kill the queen. Without their head, the attacked Ants accept the presence of the other species which gradually replace them completely. Other species, which cannot manage on their own, behave even worse. The so-called Amazon Ants are slave-makers which are looked after in their own nests by individuals captured from other species and reduced to a state of servitude. Ants have very varied feeding habits. Many species are carnivorous, but others prefer fungi (the South American *Atta* has already been mentioned), seeds and in particularly sugary substances; some species have a symbiotic relationship with Aphids and feed on their honeydew.

Ants of the genus *Myrmecocystus* are of great interest. They use some of their workers to store liquids. The abdomen of these individuals is grotesquely distended and filled with reserve substances. When a worker needs to feed it goes to one of these living reservoirs which supplies food by regurgitation.

▼ Honey-pot Ants

## Termites

Termites, the last group of social insects to be discussed, are markedly different from Bees, Wasps and Ants, which are all closely related members of Hymenoptera. They have many common structural characteristics and their societies are basically similar. Termites, on the other hand, are in evolutionary terms far removed from Hymenoptera. They belong to the order Isoptera and if anything might be considered nearest to cockroaches.

The basic difference concerns development. Termites only undergo partial metamorphosis and do not pass through the larva and pupa stages, which in the social species of Hymenoptera are totally dependent on adult care. Young Termites are already able to work without being a burden on the community.

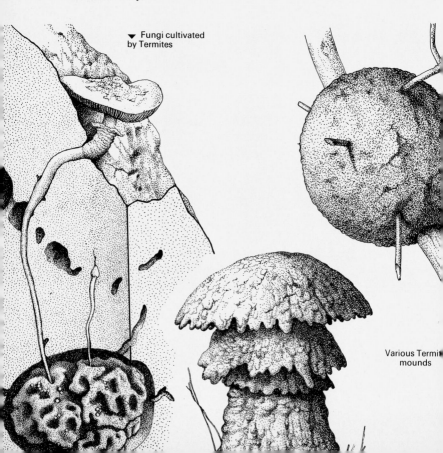

▼ Fungi cultivated by Termites

Various Termite mounds

Bee, Ant and Wasp societies are essentially matriarchal. The male role is confined to reproduction, since the workers are all sterile females. With Termites, however, the males play an important active part in the work of the community in that some belong to the sterile castes, while the fertile individuals stay near the female which has to be fertilized several times during her life.

Termites live mainly in hot regions of the world. There are only three species in Europe, but many more in tropical regions. They are commonly called White Ants, suggesting they are social insects and usually pale in colour and slightly translucent. This last characteristic is related to the fact that Termites rarely live in the open. Most species always stay underground or inside wood. Termites can be divided into four basic castes. First, there are the males and females destined for

▼ *Bellicositermes* castes

Queen

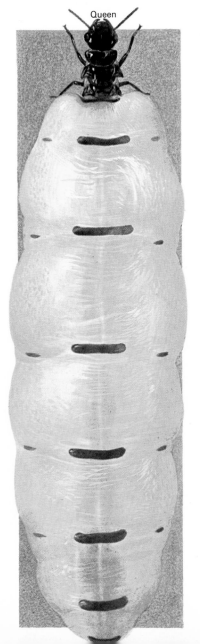

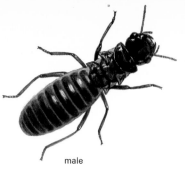

male

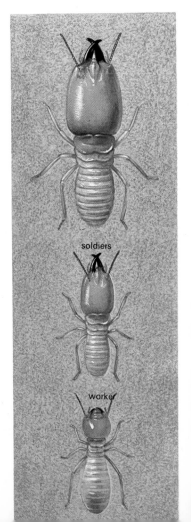

soldiers

worker

reproduction. They have long wings, the hind pair very similar to the front ones, and these are only used for swarming, the means which ensures the necessary dispersal of the species. Swarming Termites provide food for many animals, including man, and few survive. The society's workers make up the third caste. Their functions are similar to the worker ants'. In some species there are no real workers, their work being performed by members of the other castes before they reach maturity.

The fourth and final caste consists of the soldiers and is the caste most typical of Termite society. The soldiers are bigger than the workers and can be distinguished by their much enlarged heads. The head often ends in powerful jaws so highly developed that they cannot be used to lift food, a task which has to be performed for the soldiers by the workers. In some species of the family Rhinotermidae the soldiers' jaws are not very developed, but instead they have a curious organ, a kind of pointed nose which squirts a sticky poisonous substance to keep enemies, especially dangerous ants, at bay. As nests, Termites build some of the most amazing constructions known in the animal world. They sometimes stand twenty feet high and are built, it should not be forgotten, by animals only a fraction of an inch in size. Not all Termites build nests, which would in any case be no use to species living inside wood. The most spectacular pinnacled constructions found all over the African savannah are made of a soil material glued together with special secretions and excrement to make them virtually unassailable. Another much-used material is a kind of wood pulp used to make the nests which hang from trees like those of *Nasutitermes*. The mushroom-shaped nest of *Cubiterms* is very unusual. Inside these nests there are complex systems of hollows, brood cells and food stores, linked by a complicated network of galleries. Each species has its own building methods and is guided by an instinct which prompts thousands of individuals to work together to produce a pre-established model. The most important chamber of the termitarium, the centre of all activity, is the royal cell in which the royal couple live. The queen has a grossly enlarged abdomen and can produce as many as 10,000 eggs a day. If one of the royal couple dies a mechanism controlled by pheromones stimulates the community to raise a new king or queen from a nymph which would otherwise become a member of a different caste. The phenomenon can also occur in large colonies where part of the society breaks away to become independent.

The main source of food is wood which is digested by means of flagellated protozoa in the intestine.

### Environmental extremes: mountain insects

Any account of insect associations must end with the insects which live in harsh, selective environments where only a few specialists survive.

Insects which live on mountain tops, above the tree line, encounter special conditions similar to those in polar regions. Their period of activity can only last a couple of months, and this obviously affects their life cycle which has to be very short. Members of different orders living at high altitudes have certain features in common. Many species for example, are apterous, in other words without functional wings. Melanism – predominantly dark coloration – is also widespread.

The first insects to be seen on a mountain trip are Butterflies. In the Alps there are many species of the genus *Erebia*, with dark brown velvety wings and slow dancing flight.

Under the stones there are many beetles, including large bronze-coloured Ground Beetles (Carabidae), slow Weevils (Curculionidae), darting Rove Beetles (Staphylinidae), together with countless Springtails (Collembola).

Ground Beetle ▶

**Desert insects**

The desert is the harshest environment for any form of life, since organisms can do without everything except water, which is the basic element of every vital function.

Even in the desert, however, some insects survive. These are animals which can reduce water loss to a minimum, either by avoiding transpiration or by excretory mechanisms which save as much liquid as possible. Beetles of the family Tenebrionidae are typical desert insects, easily distinguished by their black colouring, sculpted crests and tubercles and often very convex shape.

Many parts of the Mediterranean region, while not quite as dry as a desert, have very sparse rainfall and are inhabited by insects which like dry conditions. For example, many members of the family Tenebrionidae, the roundish *Pimelia*, the flat-backed *Akis*, and *Asida* with its sculpted elytra. Many of these species are nocturnal and hide under stones during the day, but others, like the agile slender-legged *Pimelia*, are the day beetles, which scurry across the bare ground in broad daylight.

◀ *Pimelia*

215

### Cave insects

Environmental conditions in underground caves are the exact opposite of desert conditions. In caves there is never any lack of water; on the contrary, caves are almost always wet. The temperature is absolutely constant, with no variations between day and night, or between seasons.

However, one grave defect limits the animal population to a minimum: the lack of light and hence of green plants. The available food is minimal and in practice consists solely of plant and animal remains carried in by water, and of the lower plants which grow on this detritus. Apart from occasional visitors, caves harbour species which can live equally well in caves or outside them.

# Insects and Man

Of all land animals not bred by man insects undoubtedly have the greatest economic effect. Millions are spent on insecticides to get rid of plant pests; insects transmit disease and by their presence affect the living conditions of entire populations.

The question arises: are men or insects more important? A banal question perhaps, but the reply can be revealing. Imagine a world without men. Almost all living things would benefit by their hypothetical disappearance and would above all be able to restore the equilibrium which has been destroyed by the presence of human beings (or, to be more exact, by the economic interests of a small number of them). But remove insects and

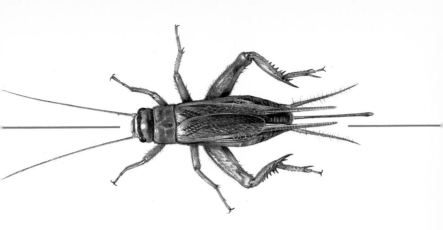

without them no natural balance could exist on land; ecological catastrophe would ensue. It could be argued that man's presence on earth is as harmful as the absence of insects would be.

So the villains are men, not insects. That is not to say that men should not fight insects which interfere with their vital interests: every animal species has to struggle for existence. But insects can never be eliminated totally, even in agricultural areas where they certainly do much damage.

Plants have flourished on dry land with the help of insects, and without them could not have survived and so found their place in nature.

219

### Disease carriers

Insects' defence weapons are rarely dangerous to man. Only the stings of a swarm of Bees or angry Wasps are potentially lethal, but these are exceptional cases. The real danger lies in the parasitic micro-organisms transmitted by blood-sucker insects which become bearers of various diseases. Lice used to be among the main disease carriers in temperate zones. The main infections they cause are epidemic typhus, trench-fever and the recurrent fever of the Mediterranean.

Fleas are carriers of even more dangerous diseases. In particular if the Rat Flea passes to man it can transmit bubonic plague. Fleas also transmit many other parasites, from bacteria to threadworm and tape-worm.

Diseases carried by insects, which are still common today, include malaria and sleeping sickness. Both are transmitted by members of the order Diptera, the former by mosquitoes of the genus *Anopheles*, the latter by flies of the genus *Glossina* (Tsetse Flies). Malaria is caused by plasmodia; Protozoa with a complex life-cycle which enter the human organism as spores in the saliva of a Mosquito as it bites its victim; they reach the liver and complete the first part of the life-cycle there. They then spread to the red corpuscles. They finally return to the Mosquito as it sucks blood and there completes the cycle of

▼ *Glossina*　　　　　　　　　　　　▼ *Aèdes aegypti*

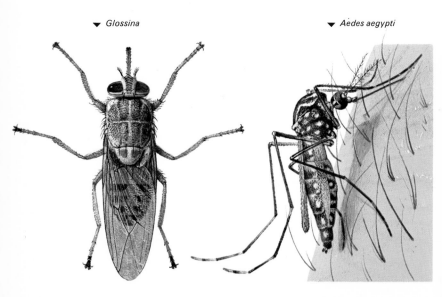

sexual development, which leads to the formation of spores
ready to return to man by means of the Mosquito's bite. There
are various types of malaria caused by different plasmodia – for
example, tertian and quartan, so-called because of the number
of days between attacks of fever. Sleeping sickness is caused by
trypanosomes, flagellate protozoa transmitted to man by the
Tsetse Fly. It, too, is a disease of the blood. Finally, another fly
which transmits a terrible disease is *Aedes aegypti*, the carrier
of yellow fever.

### Plant parasites

It would take more than a few lines to describe the insects
which attack plants and harm agriculture. There are hundreds
of pages on the subject in any book on phytopathology, the
science of plant diseases. Here, only the main aspects of the
problem can be discussed, with a reminder of the dangers of
species brought from their country of origin.

This is illustrated by the case of the Chrysomelid potato
beetle, commonly called the Colorado Beetle. This large yellow
beetle with black stripes, which spread to Europe at the end of
the last century, is the main enemy of the potato, eating its
leaves both as larva and as adult. Another typical case is
*Corythuca ciliata*, a small fragile-looking bug which appeared

▼ Trypanosome

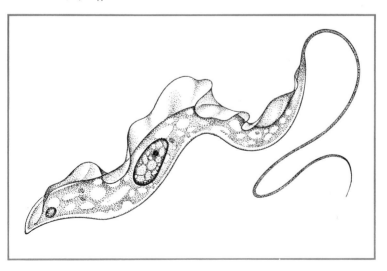

▼ Grain Weevil

▲ Colorado Beetle

in Italy a few years ago and spread rapidly. Its bite causes the yellowing of plane leaves, so that even the city-dweller is aware of this insect's presence. Methods of fighting these insects have depended on the use of very strong poisons. Besides being dangerous to human health, these have encouraged increasingly resistant strains, among insect species.

▼ Cottony Cushion Scale attacked by *Rodolia cardinalis*

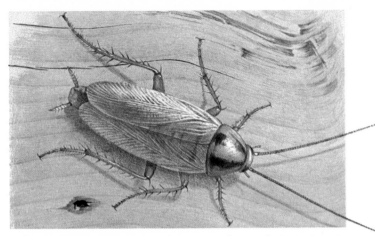

▲ German Cockroach (*Blattella*)    ▼ Common Cockroach (*Blatta*)

### Household insects

The attics and damp cellars of old houses are favourite places for many small animals and while the mouse is the classic inhabitant, many insects select these surroundings too. These are usually insects which like the dark; many feed on detritus and remains, but there are carnivores too. They belong to most orders. There are members of Apterygota, like the Bristletail, *Thermobia domestica*, or Firebrat which is flat and slippery, with a covering of scales all over its body.

The House Cricket, *Acheta domestica*, Orthoptera, differs from its country relation in its pale speckled colouring and slimmer form. Termites invade human dwellings too, especially when there is plenty of wood for them to feed on and a damp atmosphere, two conditions found in Venice where, sadly enough, these insects have done some damage.

Everyone knows Cockroaches, some of the most unpopular household insects. The German Cockroach (*Blattella*) likes to live in restaurants and cafés where it finds warmth and plenty of food. A fair number of beetles are household insects, including the large, slow *Blaps* which likes cellars and the strange *Gibbium* and *Tenebrio* which live in flour.

▼ *Gibbium*

## Useful insects

There are, perhaps, more insects which can be described as useful than might be expected, although they are usually misunderstood. Often their actions are indirectly beneficial, as with all the parasites which attack other harmful insects and are scarcely noticed. Species eaten in hot countries are directly useful, they include Grasshoppers which thus make up for some of the damage done by migrations. When thousands of Termites swarm they too are collected and eaten.

The use of silk is very ancient in origin, dating back to the

▼ Life cycle of the Silk Moth

third millenium BC. The silk worm is simply the caterpillar of *Bombyx mori*, a moth of the family Bombycidae which reached Rome at the time of Justinian. Since then, breeding silk worms has been a typical country pursuit in Italy. Until comparatively recently the silk mill was an important element of rural economy, and one of the few professional outlets for the female work force.

Bees used to be extremely important as producers of honey, since this was the only substance used for sweetening before sugar was available.

▼ Silk Worm, the caterpillar of the Silk Moth

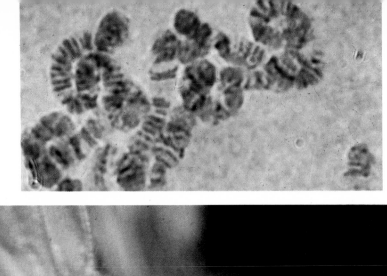

## Laboratory insects

The last insect to be discussed is the Midge, which everyone regards as the smallest, most useless and most insignificant of insects.

The only time it becomes important is when it gets in someone's eye and ends its dull life in a flood of tears.

Observant entomologists during the last century noticed in the salivary glands of *Chironomous* larvae (one of the many Midge species) strange formations of filaments in transverse bands. More recently these filaments were identified as giant chromosomes. Chromosomes are, of course, the seat of genetic control in the cells, so it was extremely useful for scientists to have such large examples to hand. Giant chromosomes were also found to be present in many species of Diptera, and for research purposes large numbers of *Drosophila*, the Vinegar Fly, began to be bred. This fly has the advantage of reproducing quickly, providing many generations in a short time. The study of chromosomes was later combined with the study of hereditary characteristics and mutations.

▼ ▶ Chironomid and
its chromosomes

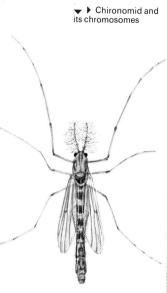

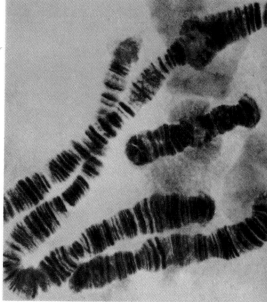

# Classification

About a million insect species have been recorded to date, but no one really knows how many species there are on Earth today. With such a range of organisms, the first problem is how to describe them and how to identify similarities and differences between them. Zoologists try to group them according to criteria which take account of their similarities and differences.

The science of zoological classification, known as taxonomy, is based on groupings which arrange organisms into an intelligible system. Insects, like other animals, are divided into a number of categories, each known as a taxon. The basic taxon, the key stone of classification, is the species, which to some

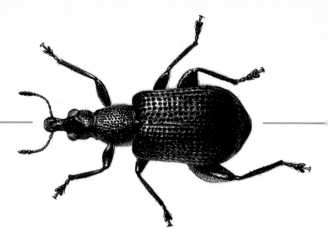

extent corresponds to something which actually exists in nature. The species includes all individuals which have common morphological and physiological characteristics and can be crossed to produce fertile offspring.

As all the individuals in a species resemble one another, even the layman can to some extent grasp what a species is. However, different insect species are often alarmingly similar. Methods of distinguishing them are gradually becoming more sophisticated. A century ago the only characteristics used in identification were external morphological characters, that is to say those which could be observed by examining the insect under a magnifying glass or at most a microscope. But sometimes there were real puzzles and other methods had to be found. An important step forward was the realization that the copulatory organs are characteristic in each species. This solved many problems, though by no means all of them. Nowadays, the sophisticated systems for identifying species involve the study of chromosomes, the electron microscope and mathematical and, more particularly, statistical methods requiring the extensive use of computers.

The next step in classification is the genus. A number of species which only have small differences between them will be grouped in a single genus. Obviously, since this taxon is not always a natural grouping, different zoologists evaluate differences and similarities differently. As there can never be total agreement among taxonomists, there is some splitting up of some old genera and grouping together of others.

The same problem occurs in the higher categories. The family is a group of genera, the order a group of families and the class a group of orders. Here we stop, because insects form a class, or in other words all belong to the class Insecta.

Beside the problems of grouping so far discussed, there is also the problem of nomenclature for the members of species, genera, families and so on.

The species is always identified by two Latin names (Latin is used to make the system of nomenclature international). The first of the two names gives the genus to which the species belongs. *Pieris brassicae*, for example, is the zoologists name for the large Cabbage White. As *Pieris* indicates the genus, other species have the same name: *Pieris rapae* and *Pieris napi* are butterflies related to the Cabbage White. In this book this system of nomenclature has been used for all insect species which are given their scientific name. The family or group of genera, always has a Latin name ending in -idae. The Cabbage White, for example, belongs to the family Pieridae. The Latin names of orders often end in -ptera, though not always. Thus family Pieridae belongs to order Lepidoptera. However, these names do enable entomologists from all countries to converse together, knowing they are talking about the same species.

These details are meant to help the reader pick a way through the mass of names which inevitably litter any work on insects. A final point is that classification does not group insects on a random basis, but brings together insects originally descended from the same stock. The system of classification is thus also a genealogical tree. The following pages summarize the characteristics of the orders which make up the insect class.

# ORDERS

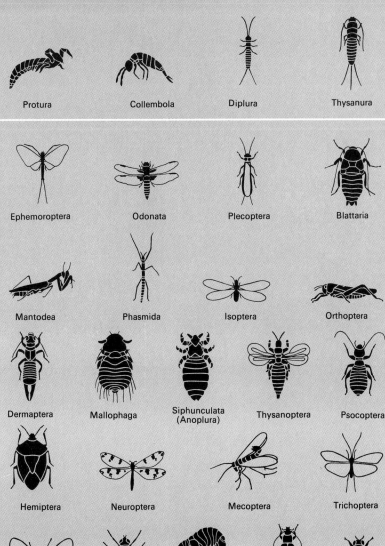

Protura

Collembola

Diplura

Thysanura

Ephemoroptera

Odonata

Plecoptera

Blattaria

Mantodea

Phasmida

Isoptera

Orthoptera

Dermaptera

Mallophaga

Siphunculata
(Anoplura)

Thysanoptera

Psocoptera

Hemiptera

Neuroptera

Mecoptera

Trichoptera

Lepidoptera

Diptera

Siphonaptera
(Aphaniptera)

Coleoptera

Hymenoptera

Primitive insects

## Protura

Primitive insects without wings or antennae. The head has no eyes or antennae. The front legs are held up and function as antennae. The abdomen of the adult consists of twelve segments, the largest number found in any insect.

Because of these characteristics many experts believe that Protura should not be classed as insects at all. Protura live in the soil and little is known about their habits. They were only discovered at the beginning of this century by Agostino Dodero.

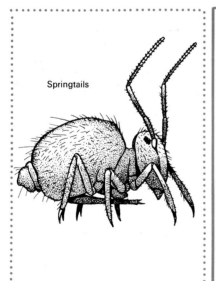

Springtails

## Collembola—Springtails

Small wingless insects which can leap. The head has moderately developed eyes and mouth parts sunk in the head capsule.

The abdomen consists of only six segments, with three special appendages: the ventral tube (on the first segment), which provides adhesion; the retinaculum (on the third segment); and the furcula (on the fifth), the springing organs. The order is divided into two sub-orders: the Arthropleona, and the Symphypleona.

## Diplura—Two-Pronged Bristle-Tails

Wingless insects with a soft flattened body and without pigment. The head has long antennae and the mouth parts are sunk inside it.

The legs are very agile so that insect can move quickly. The abdomen ends in two appendages (or cerci) which may be long and slender or short and robust.

The order is divided into three families: Campodeidae, Japygidae, and Projapygidae. Diplura all live in the soil, under stones or in rotting material.

## Thysanura—Bristle-Tails

Wingless insects, with a soft body covered by scales. The head has long antennae and mouth parts of the biting type.

The legs are short but the insect is agile. The abdomen, consisting of eleven segments, ends in three appendages: two very elongated cerci and, between them, the modified last segment.

The order is divided into two families: the Machilidae in which the prothorax is enlarged to form a hump, and the Lepismidae in which the body is flattened. Thysanura live in a variety of environments.

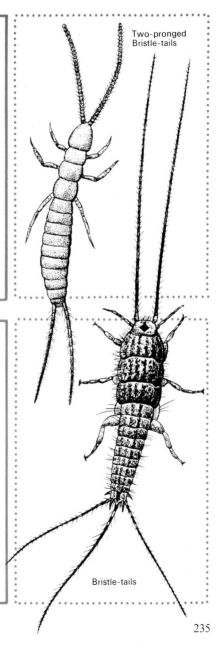

Two-pronged Bristle-tails

Bristle-tails

235

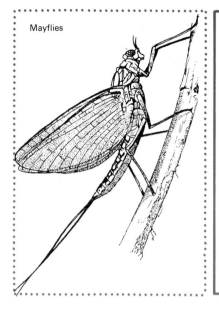

Mayflies

### Ephemeroptera—Mayflies
These are the most primitive winged insects and the only ones which moult after they have acquired their wings. The head has short antennae. The adult mouth parts are often not functional.

There are generally four wings, but some species have only two.

The abdomen ends in two or three cerci (long processes), one of which is the modified last abdominal segment.

The nymphs live in running or stagnant water. They breathe the oxygen in the water by means of tracheal gills on the sides of the abdomen.

Dragonflies

### Odonata—Dragonflies
The head has mouth parts of the biting type, short antennae and large compound eyes covering almost the entire surface of the head.

The thorax bears slender legs and two pairs of large membranous wings with a close network of veins.

The male abdomen has the reproductive organ at the base rather than the tip.

The nymphs are aquatic and breathe oxygen dissolved in the water by means of tracheal gills.

The order is divided into two sub-orders: Zygoptera and Anisoptera.

## Plecoptera—Stoneflies

Insects found near water, in which they pass their early stages.

Characteristically, they are flattened in shape and have large wings which they hold flat over the body when at rest. The head has mouth parts of the biting type, often rather reduced, and compound eyes and ocelli. The two pairs of wings are membraneous. The abdomen ends in two cerci developed in various ways. The larvae live in cold oxygenated fresh water and generally feed on plants, although some are carnivorous.

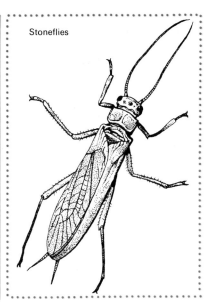

Stoneflies

## Dictyoptera:
## Blattodea—Cockroaches

Characteristically, the body is flattened and has long cursorial legs with spines.

The head is usually hidden under the prothorax and has a pair of long filiform antennae.

The wings are developed in various ways, and there are some species without wings, especially in the females.

The abdomen ends in lobes or styli. The oothecae, made in various shapes by the females, are also a characteristic feature.

Cockroaches are mainly found in the hotter parts of the world.

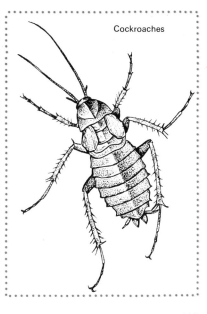

Cockroaches

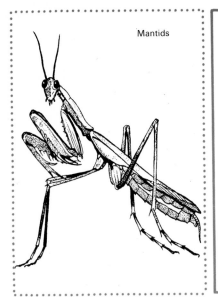

Mantids

### Dictyoptera: Mantodea—Mantids

Insects fairly similar to grasshoppers but with some different features related to their predatory habits. The head is triangular, and highly movable with mouth parts of the biting type.

In European species, the prothorax is very long and narrow, but among exotic fauna there are species with a broad expanded prothorax.

The prothorax bears a pair of raptorial legs adapted for capturing other insects.

The wings are well developed, especially the hind pair.

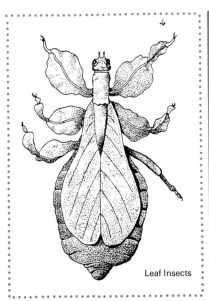

Leaf Insects

### Phasmida—Stick insects

Phasmida includes insects which are among the most outstanding examples of mimicry. The famous Stick and Leaf Insects belong to this order. Stick Insects have an exceptionally long body with slender, delicate legs, while Leaf Insects have a flattened body with reliefs like leaf venation, and leaf-like legs.

These insects are usually green or brown and move very slowly. There are some parthogenetic species in which males only appear irregularly. They are among the few insects which can regenerate mutilated limbs.

## Isoptera—Termites

As Termites are social insects, the individuals in each species are divided into castes, consisting of fertile individuals (kings and queens) and sterile individuals (soldiers and workers).

In the sterile castes, the head is usually eyeless. In soldiers, the jaws are powerfully developed, except in those which have to produce sticky liquid.

Only the fertile individuals have wings which are used for swarming, and then lost.

Termites usually feed on wood which they are able to digest.

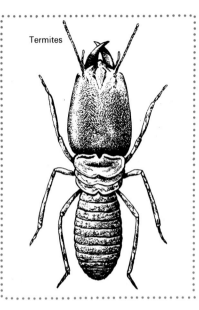

Termites

## Dermaptera—Earwigs

The head has mouth parts of the biting type and long antennae. The legs are developed normally and adapted for running. The first pair of wings are very short and are not adapted for flight.

In the resting position, the second pair are elaborately folded under the first.

The abdomen ends in a pair of strong pincers formed by modified cerci.

The pincers take different forms, not only in individuals of different sexes, but in individuals of the same sex.

Earwigs usually live in plant detritus or under bark.

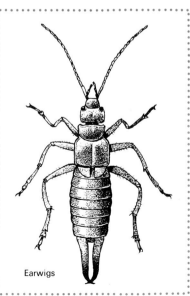

Earwigs

239

Grasshopper

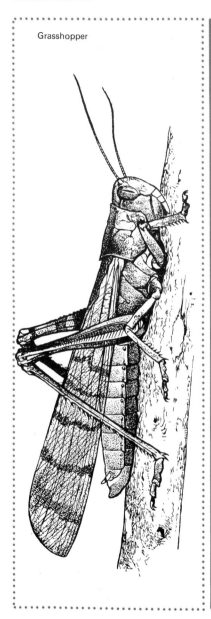

## Orthoptera—Grasshoppers, Crickets and Locusts

The head has typical biting mouth parts, with strong, well-developed mandibles.

The thorax has three pairs of legs, the first two developed normally, while the last pair is modified as a springing organ with large muscular femur and strong dentate tibia. The front wings are long, narrow and fairly tough. They are known as the tegmina. They have a protective function and are often used in the emission of sound. The hind wings are well developed and are folded like a fan when at rest. Many species do not have wings adapted for flight; they may have reduced wings or none at all.

In many species there is a gregarious instinct, with the formation of both a gregarious and a solitary phase.

The order is divided into two sub-orders. The sub-order Ensifera is distinguished by the females' long ovipositors which are flattened and blade-like in Tettigoniidae, and needle-like in Gryllidae. The family Gryllidae also includes the Molecricket, which has forelegs adapted for digging.

The sub-order Caelifera is distinguished by the short antennae and barely developed ovipositor.

## Mallophaga—Biting Lice and Bird Lice

Wingless parasitic insects of warm-blooded vertebrates. The body is flattened with a large head and short antennae. The mouth parts are of a modified biting type. The legs have short tarsi with claws. The abdomen is often broad at the end.

Members of Mallophaga live on mammals and more often on birds.

As they have mouth parts of the biting type they cannot suck their host's blood, but instead feed on flakes of skin, feathers and hair.

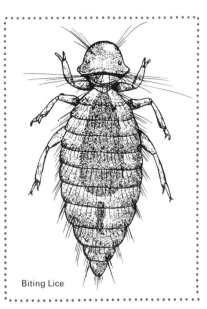

Biting Lice

## Anoplura—Sucking Lice

The parasites known as lice belong to this order. The characteristics are a flattened body and a special leg structure.

The head has short antennae and mouth parts of the sucking type.

The legs end in a claw which, together with the extended tibia, forms a kind of pincer, so that the insect can grip into its host's hairs.

They are all parasites of mammals, and only marsupials are free of lice.

There are two species of human parasite: *Pediculus humanus* and *Phthirus pubis*.

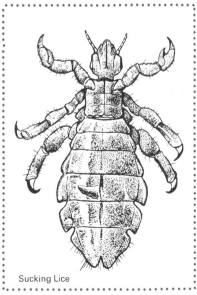

Sucking Lice

Thrips

**Thysanoptera—Thrips**
Small insects with characteristic mouth parts and wings. The head has a pair of short antennae and very modified mouth parts, partly sunk in the head capsule. They have a sucking function.

The wings are very narrow with long fringes.

Metamorphosis in Thysanoptera is unusual, falling somewhere between partial and total metamorphosis.

These insects usually live on plants, but some are found in decomposing substances. Some species damage cultivated plants.

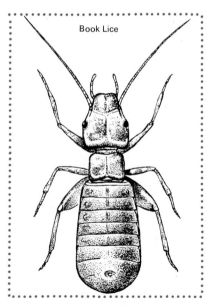

Book Lice

**Psocoptera—Psocids or Book lice**
Small insects with long filiform antennae. There are both compound eyes and simple ocelli on the head.

The mouth parts are of the biting type, slightly modified.

Some forms are wingless, and when wings do occur they are held folded roof wise over the abdomen.

Psocoptera are fairly common under bark, but are also often found in houses, in books, under old pictures and even among food stuffs. Some are found in insect collection cases, where they feed on the glue.

242

## Hemiptera—True Bugs: Homoptera

Zoologists cannot agree whether or not Homoptera and Heteroptera form a single order – Hemiptera (or Rhynchota). Without pre-judging the issue, the division into two groups here is purely a matter of convenience.

Homoptera includes a wide range of insects characterized by mouth parts of the piercing and sucking type, which are known as a rostrum. They are subdivided into two: Auchenorrhyncha and Sternorrhyncha. In Auchenorrhynca, the rostrum clearly arises from the head. Some of the main families should be mentioned. The Fulgoridae are often distinguished by ostentatious head appendages and beautifully coloured wings. The Cicadidae include the common Cicada, well known for its stridulation. The Membracidae have large appendages on the prothorax, often shaped like thorns. They are leaping insects, like members of other families of Auchenorrhyncha.

In Sternorrhyncha the rostrum apparently arises from between the front legs. This series includes the family Psyllidae, which are like miniature, agile Cicadas and often damage plants; the aphids, plants pests in which the generations alternate.

Cicada

243

Bugs

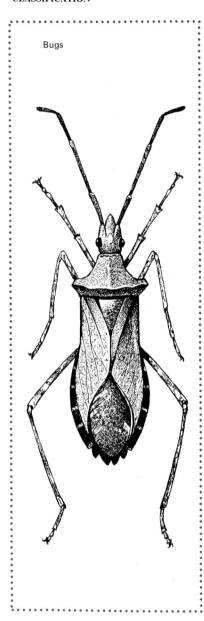

## Hemiptera—True Bugs: Heteroptera

These insects are distinguished by the mouth parts and wing structure. The head has mouth parts of the piercing and sucking type in the form of a rostrum or snout. The legs are of various types, depending on the species' environment. The front wings have a thick, hardened base and membranous tip. They are called hemielytra and have a protective function.

The abdomen is developed normally and is often brightly coloured under the wings.

A considerable number of Heteroptera live in water but breathe atmospheric oxygen. They include the flat-bodied Water Scorpion of the family Nepidae; the Noteonectidae which have long hind legs used as oars; the enormous tropical Belostomatidae.

The members of the families Gerridae and Veliidae are surface-dwelling species.

The Cimicidae have very short wings and are blood-sucking parasites (Bed-bugs).

The Reduviidae have a large curved rostrum and are all predators (Assassin Bugs).

The Pentatomidae or Plant Bugs are distinguished by their round and often brightly coloured bodies.

The Lygaeidae are the most prominent group of Heteroptera.

## Neuroptera—Alder Flies, Snake Flies and Lacewing Flies

This is the first group so far in this section which undergoes complete metamorphosis.

Members of Neuroptera are distinguished by their large membranous wings with a close network of veins. The mouth parts are of the biting type. The prothorax may be developed normally, but is sometimes very long and narrow (in Raphidiidae and Mantispidae).

The legs are usually normal, but are modified for catching prey in Mantispidae.

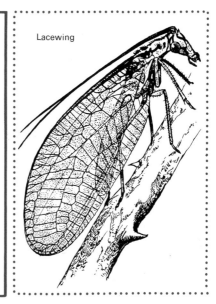

Lacewing

## Mecoptera—Scorpion Flies

Insects with long bodies and slender legs. The head is prolonged into a rostrum.

The mouth parts are of an atypical biting kind. The wings are membranous and transparent with dark patches.

In male *Panorpa*, the abdomen ends in a kind of pincer which looks like a scorpion's tail.

Some insects, members of the family Boreidae, have legs suitable for leaping, and no wings. They are active during the cold months.

Members of Mecoptera are generally carnivorous.

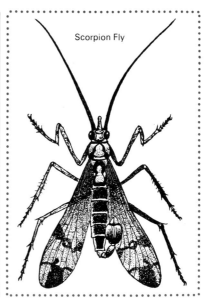

Scorpion Fly

Caddis Fly

**Trichoptera—Caddis flies**

Insects similar to moths, with aquatic larvae. The head has long thread-like antennae, compound eyes and simple ocelli. The mouth parts are often reduced and often have no mandibles.

The legs are generally long and slender.

The wings are membranous and are held over the back in a roof shape when at rest. They are covered in hairs – the name Trichoptera, from the Greek, means 'hairy wings'.

The larvae which are not unlike caterpillars live in water, where they breathe dissolved oxygen.

The cases which these larvae build themselves are characteristic. They are made of different materials, depending on the insects' surroundings. In streams they often use pebbles and in still water plant detritus.

Some larvae do not fit this scheme, either because of the shape of their body or because they do not build cases. Tricoptera larvae are carnivorous or feed on plant detritus.

Adult caddis flies often fly at twilight.

## Lepidoptera—Butterflies and Moths

In these insects, the head has long, slender mouth parts of the sucking type, with a proboscis which is coiled up when at rest. Only a few primitive species have biting mouth parts. There are always large compound eyes and sometimes simple ocelli. There are various types of antennae – clavate, filiform or pectinate. The thorax has three pairs of legs, which in some species are poorly developed and hardly adapted for walking.

The wings, always four in number, are membranous and covered all over with little overlapping coloured scales which form the well-known patterns.

The larvae, or caterpillars, have two or four pairs of characteristic abdominal prolegs and three pairs of legs on the thorax. Order Lepidoptera is divided into two suborders, Homoneura and Heteroneura.

Homoneura covers the most primitive members, with similar hind and forewings.

The members of Heteroneura are much more numerous. They include most known species which for practical purposes can be divided into Microlepidoptera (including some of the smallest species), Butterflies and Moths.

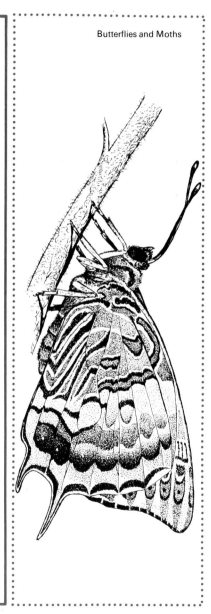

Butterflies and Moths

247

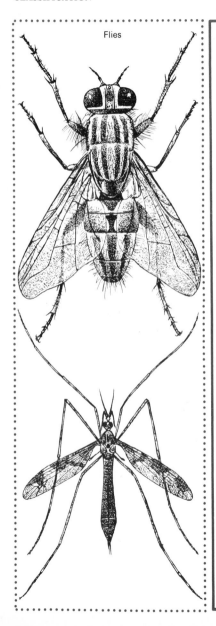

Flies

## Diptera—Two-winged Flies or True Flies

This order includes the insects known as Flies and Mosquitoes. They are distinguished by having only a single pair of functional wings. The head has compound eyes developed in various ways and ocelli.

The mouth parts may be of the lapping type (in House Flies and Blue-bottles) or of the sucking and piercing type (in Mosquitoes, Horseflies and Tsetse Flies). The antennae are usually modest in size and sometimes feathery. The thorax has legs which are sometimes long and slender, but are more normally developed.

There are always two wings, except in the small number of species which are wingless. The wings are attached to the mesothorax and are generally membranous and transparent. On the metathorax, there are various forms of small expansions known as halteres which are modified hind wings.

There are two basic types of larvae. In some the head is distinct, while the other is so reduced that the larvae seems to have no head at all. In this case, the mouth parts are highly modified as well.

The pupae of many members of Diptera are protected by a special case known as a puparium.

248

## Siphonaptera (Aphaniptera)
## Fleas

These insects are distinguished by the shape of the body which is flattened from side to side, and by their fawn colour and long legs adapted for leaping.

The head is flat like the body. The antennae are very short and the eyes consist of a single ommatidium. The mouth parts are of the piercing and sucking type. The head often ends in a series of large bristles.

The thorax is always wingless and has long, powerful legs. The abdomen consists of ten segments. The structure of the last three is very distinctive.

The larvae have no legs and resemble the larvae of Diptera. Fleas are external parasites of warm-blooded animals found especially on mammals, but on birds too. They can often live on more than one host. One species buries itself under the skin and remains there as a subcutaneous parasite. All fleas feed on blood.

The larvae live in detritus, inside dens, nests or dwellings.

Fleas

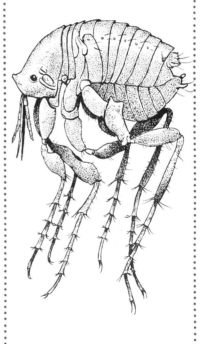

Beetles

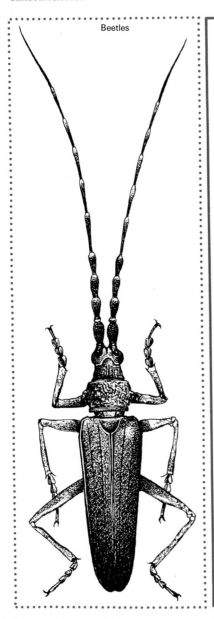

**Coleoptera—Beetles**

Insects distinguished by their hard elytra which are modified forewings, and usually tough integument. The head has mouth parts of the biting type, a pair of compound eyes developed in various ways and a pair of antennae.

The legs on the thorax are very varied in form and size. The back of the prothorax is always hardened, while the back of the meso- and mesothorax is soft. The forewings are very hard; they have lost their primitive flying function and serve mainly as a protective shield (elytra). The hindwings are membranous and used in flight, but they are very often missing. The abdomen is generally soft on the back, protected by the elytra, and tough underneath.

The larvae of Coleoptera are very varied in form. These insects live in all land and fresh water environments and have a very wide range of feeding habits. Many species are carnivorous and predatory; these include members of the family Carabidae.

Others are phytophagous or xylophagous. This group includes the families Chrysomelidae, Cerambycidae and Curculionidae. Very many beetles live in decomposing materials like dung (the Scarabaeidae) or corpses (the Silphidae).

## Hymenoptera—Bees, Wasps, Ants and others

These insects are fairly variable in form and are often social in their habits. The head has ocelli and compound eyes and a pair of antennae, also variable in form, but often filiform or geniculate. The mouth parts may be of the biting type, or biting and lapping as in Bees.

The thorax has legs which are usually cursorial and often long and agile.

There are four wings which are membranous, with reduced venation. The wings may be absent, especially in female individuals or worker ants. The abdomen is variable in form and in females has an ovipositor which is sometimes highly developed and is transformed into a sting with related poison glands in the group Aculeata.

There are various types of larva in Hymenoptera. The larvae of many Sawflies (sub-order Symphyta) resembles caterpillars and have abdominal prolegs, while those characteristic of Aculeata in particular have no appendages at all. The order Hymenoptera is divided in two sub-orders. The sub-order Symphyta consists mainly of the phytophagous species. These insects are distinguished by the absence of a 'waist'.

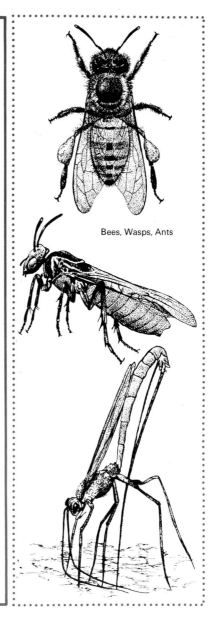

Bees, Wasps, Ants

251

# Bibliography

**General Reference Works**

Imms, A. D. *A General Text Book of Entomology, 9th ed.* (revised by O. W. Richards and G. Davies.) Methuen, 1970

Commonwealth Scientific and Industrial Research Organisation, *The Insects of Australia, A Text Book for students and research workers.* Melbourne University Press, 1970

Chinery, M. Field *Guide to the Insects of Britain and Northern Europe.* Collins, 1973

Handbooks for the Identification of British Insects, published by the Royal Entomological Society of London

Joy, N. H. *A Practical Handbook of British Beetles.* Witherby & Co., 1932 (recently re-issued in facsimile)

Killington, F. J. *A Monograph of the British Neuroptera 2 vols.* Ray Society monographs, 1936

Macan, T. T. *Key to the adults of British Trichoptera.* Freshwater Biological Association publication No. 28, 1973

Ragge, D. R. *Grasshoppers, Crickets and Cockroaches of the British Isles.* Frederick Warne & Co., 1965

Riley, N. and Higgins, L. G. *Field Guide to the Butterflies of Britain and Europe.* Collins, 1970

Southwood, T. R. E. and Leston, D. *Land and Water Bugs of the British Isles.* Frederick Warne & Co., 1973

Vari, L. *South African Lepidoptera, Vol. 1. Lithocolletidae.* Transvaal Museum Memoir, 1961

Vari, L. *South African Lepidoptera, Vol. 1. Lithocolletidae.* Transvaal Museum Memoir, 1961

Watson, A. and Whalley, P. *Dictionary of Butterflies and Moths.* Michael Joseph, 1975


**Physiology**

Wigglesworth, V. B. Insect Physiology, Methuen, 1956


**Economic Entomology**

Anderson, R. *Forest and Shade Tree Entomology.* Wiley & Sons, 1960

Pfadt, R. E. *Fundamentals of Applied Entomology.* Macmillan, 1971

Smit, B. *Insects of Southern Africa: How to control them.* Cape Town, 1964

Smith, K. G. V. *Insects and other Arthropods of Medical Importance.* British Museum (Natural History), 1973

## Ecology

Varley, G. C., Gradwell, G. R. and Hassell M. P. *Insect Population Ecology, an analytical approach* Blackwell Scientific Publications, 1973

## Collecting

Oldroyd, H., *Collecting, Preserving and Studying Insects.* Hutchinson. 1958 reprinted 1970

## Other works

Bechyne, T., ed. C. von Hayek *Guide to Beetles.* Thames & Hudson, 1956

Blackman, R. *Aphids.* Ginn & Co., 1974

Evans, H. E. *Life on a little-known Planet.* Dutton & Co., 1968

Free, J. B. and Butler, C. G. *Bumblebees.* Collins 'New Naturalist' series, 1959

Ford, E. B. *Insect Natural History.* Collins 'New Naturalist' series, 1947

Lewis, T. *Thrips, their Biology, Evolution and Economic Importance.* Academic Press, 1973

Oldroyd, H. *The Natural History of Flies.* Weidenfeld & Nicholson, 1950

Wigglesworth, V. B. *The Life of Insects.* Weidenfeld & Nicholson, 1964

Wilson, E. O. *The Insect Societies.* Harvard University Press, 1971

# Index

254

# INDEX